A Guide For Parents
of Troubled Children

A Guide For Parents of Troubled Children

Working With A Child Psychiatrist

Sylvia A. Dygert Manalis, M.D.

A Guide For Parents of Troubled Children

1603 Capitol Ave., Suite 310 Cheyenne, Wyoming USA 82001
1-888-980-6523 | admin@urlinkpublishing.com

URLink Print and Media is committed to excellence in the publishing industry.

Book design copyright © 2019 by URLink Print and Media. All rights reserved.

Published in the United States of America
ISBN 978-1-64367-359-2 (Paperback)
ISBN 978-1-64367-358-5 (Digital)
24.04.19

DEDICATION

To my mother, Ruth Evelyn Tower Dygert, who
taught me to enjoy language and children.

To my father, George Wendell Dygert, who taught me
to be independent and to think outside the box.

To my family for cheering me on.

To my writing friends, who helped me find
my path to writing this book.

I would like to thank my granddaughter,
Stephanie Paola Manalis, for drawing the
puzzle part of the front cover.

Contents

PREFACE

As MY RETIREMENT from a forty year career as a child psychiatrist began, I was looking for an activity that would teach me new skills to develop the right side of my brain, which had long been neglected as a result of focusing my life on science. A local newsletter listed a creative nonfiction writing class that was being offered by a Chicago college. I was not even sure what creative nonfiction was, but I joined this class, being open to where it might lead me. When the class ended, most students and our teacher decided to meet each week as a group to further develop our writing skills. Some ten years later that path took me to the book you are reading now.

Early in the writing group I experimented with poetry and memoir. As I followed further along this new path, I discovered an interest in writing about the many families who have shared their lives with me in my role as their child psychiatrist. These stories of families under stress and of our journeys together to improve their lives is the heart of my book,

A Guide for Parents of Troubled Children: Working with a Child Psychiatrist.

The first goal of my book is to educate families about childhood emotional problems. Through this teaching, I wish to leave behind something of value for the younger generations—a legacy of sorts— to help young families do what they can to optimize their children's emotional development. Parents can learn through my clinical experiences with the many families who have shared with me their concerns about their children. For example, Chapter Four tells the stories of four children of various ages, Ellen, Sarah, Katie and John, who have Attention Deficit Hyperactivity Disorder (ADHD). Their stories are told through conversations I have with each child and his parents as I gather data to diagnose the problem, and then present treatment suggestions for the ADHD symptoms. Some children I see only for a few sessions because they drop out or move away. Most I see over the course of several months, and a few for three or four years. So some stories will feel abbreviated, while others will have some depth.

The second goal has to do with me looking back over my career of almost fifty years in science, medicine, and psychiatry, trying to make sense of my life. Have I met my goal of helping sick people, as my teenage idol, Dr. Albert Schweitzer, had done, healing the sick in Africa?

What has my career meant to me? When I was traveling the road as a fulltime psychiatrist, I was too busy managing my private practice and my family to look at the big picture. I was immersed in the intellectual demands and intense focus necessary to the work of a psychiatrist. Now, in my writing, I can be more playful and thoughtful about the small humans who have walked through my office door to sit across from me and answer my many and difficult questions. The openness and frankness of these children have surprised, amazed, and delighted me. Their dilemmas have brought me puzzles to solve and challenges to surmount in our work together. Had I become a pediatrician, which I considered doing some fifty years ago, I'd have missed having opened to me the fascinating inner mental workings of my small patients.

I am grateful to the many families who have shared their lives with me and who are now sharing their stories with you. I also want to thank my writing group, led by Professor Re'Lynn Hansen of Columbia College, for holding my hand as I explored becoming a writer. Their encouragement and feedback were critical to me as a novice writer. The group helped me believe that what I was writing was important and could be of interest and help to others. I also am grateful to Stephanie Manalis for her art work on the cover, to Rich Manalis for his photograph of the author, and to Mary Dygert and Janean Laidlaw who gave me valuable writing guidance.

Sylvia Anne Dygert Manalis

CHAPTER ONE

Should I Take My Child to a Psychiatrist?

THIS BOOK FEATURES stories about children with emotional and behavioral problems with whom I have worked over the past forty years as a child psychiatrist. The stories tell of the struggles of these children and their families and of their journeys with me alongside them striving toward improved mental health. The parents of my child and teenage patients have consented to my sharing their stories with you, hoping this sharing will lighten your load as you make decisions about your own child.

This book is also about how I, in my role as a child psychiatrist, think about and understand my patients' emotional problems. But I will go beyond the clinical view and share some of my feelings about my work with families. This story-telling approach is in contrast to the approach taken in recent books written by child psychiatrists who write in a heavily scientific manner, making the prose dry and too technical for many readers. I tell you how my patients look and I relate conversations I have with them and their families, which I hope will serve to bring the stories alive.

I believe that the stories I weave about children in this book are an engaging and understandable way to convey to you, parents of a troubled child, an overview of children's emotional problems. And you may find your child in one of these stories, whether your child is having many temper tantrums a day or whether your child can't sit still long enough to be read a book or is depressed, shy or worried.

You may wonder: "Are my child's behaviors or emotions such that we need to seek help from a psychiatrist?" This collection of stories about children and families will assist you in sorting out which of your child's problems she may outgrow as she matures, versus those that are major problems and require professional assistance. The vast majority of children - nine out of ten - will go through their growing up years without needing psychiatric intervention. My stories are about the one out of ten children who have emotional and behavioral problems of a serious nature and need professional help to move beyond them. If you have been sitting on the fence about seeking professional help, this book can help you make an informed decision.

American parents were asked in a survey if they felt any of their children had a severe behavioral or emotional problem (America's Children: Key National Indicators of Well-Being 2005 at www. nimh.nih.gov). Five out of every one hundred families suspected that one of their children had severe emotional or behavioral problems. Psychiatrists estimate that twice that number of children have an emotional problem serious enough to warrant mental disorder diagnoses and mental health treatment. Based on the psychiatrists' estimate that ten out of one hundred children have emotional problems, a school classroom of thirty children has on average three children with mental disorders.

In one study researchers concluded that a number of psychiatric services have been proven to be of help to children and teens (Jon McClellan, M. D. Psychiatric Times, September 2005, Vol. XXII, Issue 10; www.psychiatrictimes.com). The helpful treatments and the conditions identified are as follows:

- Medications for Attention Deficit Hyperactivity Disorder are proven to help children and teens.
- Antidepressant medicine combined with cognitive-behavioral therapy is proven to improve depression in teens and children.

- Antipsychotic medicine helps decrease aggression in autistic children.
- Antidepressant medicine is proven to help children with anxiety disorders.
- Several antidepressant medicines help children and teens with obsessive-compulsive disorder.
- Psychotherapy treatments proven to be most helpful for children and families are cognitive-behavioral therapy and parent training.
- Cognitive-behavioral therapy has been proven helpful for childhood depression, anxiety, posttraumatic stress disorder and conduct disorder.
- Intensive mental health services for youth with conduct and drug problems show benefits.

The effectiveness of other mental health treatments are yet to be proven. Continued research is critical in telling us which treatments help and which ones do not.

Throughout each child's story, I have sprinkled scientific information to enlighten you about the particular mental disorder highlighted by the story. Recommended sources for additional information on a given diagnosis or treatment can be found on websites of the National Institute of Mental Health (www.nimh.nih. gov) and The American Academy of Child and Adolescent Psychiatry (www.aacap.org).

You will notice that most of the stories in this book are about boys. Families across America seek psychiatric treatment for sons twice as often as they do for their daughters. Most childhood emotional problems are equally distributed among boys and girls, with three important exceptions: more boys than girls have Attention Deficit Hyperactivity Disorder, Oppositional Defiant Disorder, and Autism. This is perhaps why mental health professionals work with more boys than girls and why your son is more likely to need a psychiatrist than is your daughter.

The information these children and their parents share with me is considered medical information and is therefore strictly confidential. To allow a child's story to become public in my book, each child's parent or legal guardian has signed a consent form. Their stories are the backbone of this book, and I thank the families for generously sharing their stories in order to help other struggling families. The patients' names and the details of their lives and those of their families have been changed in order to protect their privacy. Dialogues have been altered and geographical information omitted for the purposes of privacy.

I am grateful to my patients for trusting me enough to share with me the details of their lives - - the sorrows, the secrets, and the triumphs. Having a family put its trust in me is one of the pleasures of my work. It gives me a sense of briefly holding their lives in my hands. But it also gives me a heavy sense of responsibility. I believe that each life is beautiful and sacred, no matter how filled with tragedy, shame or grief, and that for most people there can be better days ahead through self-inspection and professional assistance to achieve change.

CHAPTER TWO

An Overview of Childhood Mental Disorders and a Discussion of Shame About Seeking Help

THE DEPARTMENT OF Health and Human Services reported in 1999 that one out of ten American children over the previous few years experienced emotional or behavioral problems severely enough to be diagnosed with mental disorders. A mental disorder is a set of symptoms that leads a psychiatrist to give a diagnosis as defined in the Diagnostic and Statistical Manual (DSM-5), a manual created by the American Psychiatric Association, a professional organization of psychiatrists. The DSM-5 manual is available to the public through the National Institute of Mental Health (www.nimh.nih. gov). The American Academy of Child and Adolescent Psychiatry, a professional organization of child psychiatrists, has a website at www.aacap.org. On it, you will find a series of "Facts for Families," describing symptoms for child and teen mental disorders and the recommended treatments for these disorders. After reading one of my stories, you can go to these websites and find the list of symptoms and treatments for the particular disorder that is illuminated by a family's story.

The most common mental disorders affecting children are disorders of anxiety, mood, and attention (Health and Human Service 1999). A child with a disorder of anxiety may experience unreasonable fears and nervousness. A child with a disorder of mood may experience depression, low self-esteem, and thoughts of suicide. A child with a disorder of attention may have low focus, be distractible, and be hyperactive. Mental problems I cover in my book are those of anxiety, mood and attention, as well as autism, defiance, hallucinations, and gender confusion. In the Appendix you will find a list of various emotions and behaviors children have and the possible corresponding psychiatric diagnoses.

Frequently in my work, I come across situations that are not specifically addressed in the Diagnostic and Statistical Manual, yet it seems to me that these situations merit discussion within the context of childhood and adolescent mental health. Therefore one of my chapters covers the common problem of children who are not effectively disciplined by parents. Another chapter covers my thoughts on grandparents raising their grandchildren, children's dreams and my experience with patients considering suicide.

Mental disorders I have chosen to omit are the sixteen childhood disorders that follow: Adjustment Disorder, Sleep Disorder, Impulse Disorder, Tic Disorder, Reactive Attachment Disorder, Feeding and Eating Disorders of Infancy, Elimination Disorder, Motor Disorder, Sensory Integration Disorder, Communication Disorder, Learning Disorder and Mental Retardation, Eating Disorder, Dissociation Disorder, Drug Addictions, and Schizophrenia.

Most people are likely to seek help for physical ailments such as a broken bone, an earache or bronchitis. In contrast, a study done in 2010 by the Substance Abuse and Mental Health Services Administration, found that only about forty percent of adults with mental illness seek help. This is an improvement from a study done fourteen years earlier, (Kessler et al, 1996) showing only thirty three percent seeking needed services. Why do people seek help for physical problems more easily than for mental disorders? Shame and embarrassment surrounding mental illness continue to be strong within our culture and keep people from seeking mental health services.

What helps parents overcome the shame barrier and feel comfortable enough to seek help for a child? Parents may bring a child for help at the insistence of the child's teacher. Parents may come, not because they feel comfortable, but because of the teacher's recommendation or urgings. Teachers often refer children who are hyperactive, defiant, or autistic. These children disrupt the classroom routine and interfere with a teacher's attempts to teach other pupils. Through the teacher's experience with a wide range of children, she can spot the disruptive child whose behavior is outside the norm. It is my observation that the student who is withdrawn, depressed, or anxious is less likely to be referred to mental health services by the teacher because such a child does not disrupt the classroom.

As the biologic causes of mental disorders have become known, people feel increasingly comfortable seeking psychiatric help. For example, the term "chemical imbalance," used to explain the brain chemistry of depression, helps people see depression as a chemical disorder rather than a psychological one. Recent research shows that many mental disorders involve genetic factors and this fact may make people more comfortable in seeking help, as they feel they do not need to attribute children's problems to their own parenting deficits.

A parent may see an antidepressant medication advertised on television and will ask me if that medicine might help his child. Advertisement seems to bring depression out into the open and to impart some knowledge about it. Or, television shows like Oprah or Dr. Phil that focus on relationship problems or depression may bring a person into treatment. Parents use the internet to gather information on childhood mental disorders and come to me much better informed than was true in the past. Perhaps the internet, television, and magazine advertising and talk shows are diminishing the shame barrier as they increase people's comfort with mental disorders.

Oprah has made heroic efforts through her television shows to increase awareness of and decrease the shame attached to mental disorders as she covers topics on family violence, suicide, eating disorders, anxiety disorders, sexual abuse, autism, and social phobia, to name but a few (see www.oprah.com). Thank you, Oprah! An Oprah show on depression that I watched dramatically reminded me of our culture's continued reluctance to bring emotional problems out of the closet and into the light of day. A television celebrity who had been silently suffering from depression described to Oprah and her audience the toll her untreated depression had taken on her as well as on her two daughters. Educating people about mental illness allows them to seek help early and with reduced shame.

CHAPTER THREE

The Psychiatrist's Way of Working

I WILL INTRODUCE you to the psychiatrist's process of gathering symptoms from a family into a framework that then leads to a diagnosis. This will teach you about the kinds of information a psychiatrist needs in order to make a diagnosis, and will prepare you for questions you may be asked about your child and your family. From the diagnosis emanates a plan of mental health treatment and a plan of medications.

I always see the child and teenager in the presence of one and preferably all parents, and even grandparents, if they live nearby and help with childrearing. Why is this important? Because I need parents to describe the child's recent behaviors and moods at home and school as well as the child's birth history and family history and the child's medical problems. The history is all-important, since blood samples and x-rays don't help make a psychiatric diagnosis yet, although in the future we doctors have hope that they may do so. If a diagnosis is unclear to me at the first appointment, I will refine it as I work over time with the child and family. A Bipolar Disorder diagnosis, for example, is difficult to make in children, and is a diagnosis over-used in my opinion, so I take several weeks or months to come to such a conclusion.

Next, after making a diagnosis, I determine a plan of treatment. What forms of psychotherapy or intensive treatment programs will be useful to the child and parents? A psychiatrist is only one of several mental health professionals who may be needed to work with a child and his family.

Outpatient services range from daily programs to weekly or monthly ones. If a child's problems are mild, she and her parents will see a counselor weekly and will see the psychiatrist for a diagnosis and for medication recommendations. If the child's problems are severe, he may need a residential program or a day-treatment program that offers daily groups that address anger management, behavior modification, and self-esteem building. The child may also benefit from access to a special education teacher, a counselor for psychotherapy, a case manager to assist the parents in finding community resources and to coordinate with the child's school, and a doctor to make a diagnosis and to recommend medications. If a patient becomes a danger to herself or to others, the child is referred to a hospital program where a patient can stay for few days, then return to the outpatient programs.

After recommending a plan of treatment, I share with the family what medications may be useful. I need a parent to understand the benefits and side effects of medicines I recommend, and to agree to start his or her child on medicine. Some parents are alarmed by the idea of their child being on medications that affect mood and behavior. Other parents feel desperate and are ready to try solutions that include medications. In family situations involving divorce, I need the consent of the parent who has sole custody, or if there is joint custody, both parents must agree to a medication for their child. If both parents cannot come to an agreement on a medication I recommend, they will need to take this issue before the court for a decision. And once a medication is begun for any child, I need parental feedback on the child's reaction to the medicine.

The medication decisions I make are sometimes simple and at other times are complex. The simple decisions are similar to following a cake recipe: that is, if X is the diagnosis, then by following a decision tree developed by the American Psychiatric Association for that diagnosis, I am advised to try Y or Z medications. In most cases. Y or Z medicine works well. However, just as the attempt to make the perfect cake can lead to a fallen one, a trial of Y or Z medicine may not improve mood or behavior. Or the side effects of Y or Z may preclude the continued use of it. This is where my decision-making becomes complex. I use my experience and judgment, knowledge from professional journals and discussions with other child psychiatrists, to develop a new medication plan.

In this book as I recommend medications, I will not give the brand or generic name of a medication, but the general category — for example: antidepressant, antipsychotic, anti-anxiety, or anti-convulsant medication. Also beyond the scope of this book is a scientific description of how the medicines work and what their side effects are.

Empathy is central to a psychiatrist's work. Empathy is imagining another person's emotional or physical pain — walking in that person's shoes, so to speak. But the most powerful empathy comes when I do not need to imagine —when I myself have experienced what my patient is describing to me. Have I felt depression? Yes, I have and I know firsthand how relentlessly dreary it is. I have been in psychotherapy and have taken an antidepressant and found both helpful. I have experienced brief periods of suicidal thoughts. I am a parent, so I know from my own experience of raising two children both the joys and the emotional pain of being a parent. I recall a period in my thirties when I had panic attacks while driving a car. I felt trapped in the car and very anxious, but thankfully this stopped after a few months.

So when a patient describes depression or anxiety, I can empathize intensely. Other patient emotions I do my best to imagine, for example, rage, mania, hallucinations, and addiction cravings.

Giving a child a sense that I respect him or her is critical I believe. My use of a child's name is an opportunity for me to offer respect. I always ask a child I interview for the first time what name he prefers to be called: "Do you like to be called Jonathan or Jon; Robert or Bobby?" When I am unfamiliar with a first name, which happens more and more frequently these days, I ask, "Am I saying your name correctly? Is it Jaqan or Jokwan?"

I have a personal conviction that a child's name is his personal property and my care in saying it correctly shows he has control over his name and that I respect this. I recently met a man in Abiqui, New Mexico, who as a boy did yard work for the famous artist, Georgia O'Keeffe. His name was Robert, but Ms. O'Keeffe insisted on calling him "Paul." Robert tried to correct her, but she answered, "You are Paul." This showed her sense of feeling superior to Robert rather than respecting his wish to be called his correct name which he preferred. How significant my concern about saying the child's name correctly is to the child, I do not know. But my effort to be correct gives me the mindset of respecting this small human being sitting before me, regardless of how much trouble he is in with his parents, the school, or the juvenile authorities. So this small, but important detail, calling my patient by the name he prefers, sets the stage for my relationship with him.

As the interview with my patient and his parents begins, the child often feels put on the hot seat as I ask his parents about their concerns. This hot seat is very difficult for most children, as you can imagine. But I want the child to understand his behavior or emotional problems as his parents see them. Some parents ask to speak to me alone about their concerns, but I almost always insist the child be present. This prevents the child feeling I am talking behind his back with his parents. As the parents describe the child's moodiness or defiance, the child may respond in one of several ways: deny the behaviors, be angry the behaviors are brought out in the open, or agree with the parents, and express the desire to improve. A child who acknowledges his problems and wishes to improve is on a good path. The child who is defensive will have more work to do.

To offset the unpleasant confrontation that the child must go through by being on the hot seat, I always end my one-hour first interview by asking the child a question most of them enjoy: "If you could have any three wishes to make you happy, or to make your life better, what would you wish for?" This often brings a smile to Suzy's face: finally a question she can enjoy!

The answers to this question of three wishes are amazing to me and tell me so much about the child! Many kids will wish to improve their behaviors at home and earn better grades at school - often the same hopes the parents have. This tells me they see themselves realistically and feel bad and want to improve. Teens often throw in world peace as a wish, as they are beginning to see the larger world in philosophical terms. Young children may want a yearned-for toy or video game; depressed children don't have enough hope to think of a wish; mentally slow children wish for an object they see in my office—something concrete. But my question about a child's hopes and wishes conveys to that child that his voice is important in this difficult journey of self-inspection, change, and healing.

I have learned through my psychiatric work over these forty years that while all humans are similar in the physical aspects of having two eyes, a nose, and a mouth, they are dissimilar and unique in the invisible aspects of their personalities. While one child's emotions and behaviors may be the same as another child's, their stories of why they feel or behave that way are never the same. One child may be depressed over his parents' divorce while another may be depressed about being bullied by other children at school. Of course we have all heard this saying: "Each person is unique." But with every new child I meet, I see the wisdom of that statement. It is this infinite variety that keeps me fascinated with my work.

Year after year of seeing patient after patient, literally hundreds or maybe thousands of people in distress, has brought me a great deal of experience with families and a certain level of confidence. Through this lens of experience I can enjoy the small steps I help a patient take towards a better life. My experience also gives me a sense of the "bigger picture" where I dream about a future time when prevention of child abuse will come about, and a future when people will seek help at an early stage of their problems because shame about seeking mental health services will be a thing of the past.

CHAPTER FOUR

Childhood Attention Deficit Hyperactivity Disorder

THIS CHAPTER WILL introduce you to the symptoms of childhood ADHD and to four children with ADHD with whom I worked.

Attention Deficit Hyperactivity Disorder Symptoms

Often has difficulty focusing on tasks for at least six months as follows:

- Often makes careless mistakes on schoolwork
- Often does not seem to listen when spoken to
- Often does not follow instructions or complete chores and schoolwork
- Often is disorganized in work
- Often avoids a task that requires sustained mental effort
- Often loses things like toys, pencils, school books, homework
- Often is distracted by noise and motion around him
- Often forgets daily routine at home and school

Is hyperactive for at least six months:

- Often fidgets with hands or feet
- Often squirms in chair
- Often cannot remain seated
- Often runs and climbs in places expected to be quiet
- Often cannot play quietly
- Often talks excessively

Is impulsive for at least six months:

- Often blurts out answers
- Often cannot wait his turn
- Often interrupts or intrudes in conversations or games

ADHD symptoms are present in all settings and have their onset prior to the age of seven. Impairment of functioning in academic and social areas must be seen. ADD has the above symptoms except hyperactivity is absent.

Adapted from DSM-5.

The Whirling Girl

Ellen, a three-and-one-half-year-old girl, whirls like a tornado into my office, with her mother following close behind. She is tiny and cute as a button, her blue eyes and white teeth a blur as she enters, touching every surface within her reach: my desk and chair, me, the scales I use to weigh kids, and a doll that is resting on my small bookcase – never lighting on anything with either her body or her attention for more than a second. She is singing, giggling, and whirling.

I've seen many hyperactive children over the years, and she is on the severe end of the spectrum. Less than three percent of girls have Attention Deficit Hyperactivity Disorder (ADHD), compared to six percent of boys, but here is one of the girls.

Ellen's mother, Mrs. Rice, a young woman in jeans and a stylish blouse, follows Ellen in, wearing a frustrated look. She futilely orders her to sit in a chair. "She's been hyper like this since she started walking when she was one year old. Two and one-half years of this," gazing at me with eyes that show her fatigue.

"What does her preschool teacher say about her?" I ask.

"She's just as hyper at school as she is at home. She can't sit for story time or for coloring a paper. At home, Ellen tries to hit and kick me whenever I tell her "no." During her temper tantrums, she bites her hand and bangs her head on the floor. I'm out of ideas for handling her."

"Tell me about the pregnancy with her. Did you use alcohol or cigarettes or any drugs during the pregnancy?" I ask.

"I didn't use alcohol or drugs, but I did smoke a pack of cigarettes a day." Mothers over recent years seem to know that alcohol can harm the fetus, but they either don't know that nicotine can do harm, or they simply can't give up this highly addictive habit. Danish researchers found that a woman who smokes during pregnancy is twice as likely to have a child with ADHD as a woman who does not smoke during pregnancy (Linnet, K. *Pediatrics,* August 2005, 116; pp 462-467). In 2002, smoking during pregnancy was reported by 11.4 percent of all women giving birth in the United States, an improvement over 1990 when 18.4 percent reported smoking during pregnancy. Teens, especially, are tempted to smoke during pregnancy. Education about nicotine's potential to damage the fetus, as well as smoke cessation programs for pregnant women, need to be promoted (2004 Center for Disease Control and Prevention). Alcohol use during pregnancy is also known to increase the chance for ADHD in a child.

"She was an easy, happy baby until she started walking. Then the hyperactivity came," Mrs. Rice says.

I ask if any family members have ADHD and learn that Ellen's father was on Ritalin as a child. ADHD is the most inherited of all childhood behavior disorders. Several genes are thought to be involved in producing ADHD (Faraone, S. Medscape Psychiatry and Mental Health, 2006;11).

"Does Ellen talk in sentences and does her teacher feel she is progressing in her learning skills?" I ask.

"Yes, she talks in sentences. She is being shy with you and doesn't want to talk right now. She still doesn't know her colors," Mrs. Rice continues.

"I want Ellen's preschool teacher to complete this ADHD checklist so I know the symptoms Ellen has in the classroom. If the teacher reports six or eight ADHD symptoms on this checklist, I will conclude that Ellen has ADHD. Then I will recommend trying a small dose of a stimulant medicine. We will know within a few days if it is calming her hyperactivity and improving her focus. The main side effect of stimulants is a suppression of appetite, so I will keep a close eye on her weight."

"Are stimulants addictive?" Ellen's mother asks. This is a common concern of parents. The stimulants have gotten more bad press than they deserve in my opinion.

"It has that potential, but studies show that when ADHD is treated properly, the child is less likely to develop drug addictions later in life than when the ADHD is left untreated.

"Let's talk now about Ellen's temper tantrums. Temper tantrums are not part of ADHD and are only occasionally improved with ADHD medication. I suggest you work on your discipline skills, for example, use time outs, instead of spankings. If Ellen hits someone or throws an object in anger, have her sit on a chair in a hallway or stand facing into a corner for three minutes

— one minute per year of her age. If she will not remain in the corner, hold her on your lap for three minutes once she is quiet. Let me show you how to hold her on your lap so you will not hurt her and she will not be able to hurt you," I suggest.

I help Ellen's mother practice restraining Ellen on her lap: "Place Ellen on your lap facing away from you; grasp Ellen's opposite wrists with your hands like this, pulling her arms firmly across her chest in an X. If Ellen kicks her legs, cross your legs over Ellen's legs. To avoid a head bang from her on your chest, keep your chest a good distance from her head. Now all she can do is spit and scream. Once she is quiet for three minutes, she can get off your lap. Only use a restraint if she refuses to sit on the chair or stand in the corner for her time out. After the restraint or time out is over, ask her, 'Why did you need a time out, Ellen?' If she won't say why, then you put into words what her misbehavior was, for example, 'Because you hit me. No hitting allowed!' Be firm in your tone of voice so she knows this is serious business. Stay calm when you give the time out or restraint.

"In four weeks when we meet, I will have Ellen practice time outs here in the office to make sure she understands the steps of the time out technique of discipline. Also at the next appointment, if her teacher has indicated she is ADHD, I will recommend starting her on ADHD medications. I always tell parents that when the medicine works, it is magic!"

"Bye, Ellen, see you soon!"

"Byyye!" her voice fading like a fast-moving train's whistle as she whirls out of my office and into the hallway, mother close behind her.

· · · · · · · · ● ● ● ● ● ● ● ● · · · · ·

It is two years later, and Ellen is six years old and in the first grade. Ellen, cute as ever with her bouncing brown curls, walks into my office with her mother, crosses to a chair and sits down. She looks happy and giggly as she does every four months when I see her to check her progress in school and her height and weight. I have her teacher complete a new ADHD checklist form once or twice a year to see if the dosage of medicine is still adequate. I have increased Ellen's stimulant dose gradually as she has gotten bigger.

"Ellen, I am pleased you can sit still in your chair today. Do you remember when you used to whirl around my office, before you were on your medicine?"

Ellen's mother looks relaxed and pleased. "The teacher and I agree that Ellen is focusing on her work and learning as she should be in first grade. At home Ellen rarely has a temper tantrum any more. She takes her time outs well and earns stickers for doing her chores."

"Ellen, I am pleased you are doing so well in school and at home. Have a good summer and I will see you in the fall at the beginning of the new school year."

The Three-Year-Old With ADHD

Sarah, a small, wiry, almost three-year-old girl, is waiting outside my office with her family. I am sitting at my desk reviewing the information the social worker recorded a few weeks ago, during her evaluation of Sarah and her family. I have developed the useful habit over these last few years of leaving my door ajar while I review a child's chart. I suppose I am eavesdropping - - listening to the interaction of Sarah and her family as they await my invitation to come in. I hear Sarah talking in a loud voice to her family and her mother telling her, "Sarah, quiet down!" Sarah continues to yell. As I lift my gaze to the hallway, I see Sarah pick up a child's blue chair she has been sitting on and hoist it up over her head. She sends it sailing through the air. While it doesn't sail very far, the defiance it delivers is as clear as a bell.

Another out-of-control almost three-year-old, I think to myself. It's amazing: such small creatures, yet how much trouble some three-year-olds can get into! Kicked out of daycare centers or preschool programs for hitting, biting, or spitting on people, or for throwing things ... found in grocery stores screaming and running through the aisles to escape frantic parents who simply want to load the grocery cart with food and return home to fix dinner. What power to embarrass parents these small beings have at their disposal.

Perhaps this is some kind of archaic survival skill, like the useless appendix, which no longer serves a purpose. I tell parents they must help tame their child's anger, a task more challenging with a child who has a stubborn temperament or a high intelligence.

"Sarah, please come in to my office with your mother and grandmother," I invite her, opening my door widely. Sarah runs fearlessly through my door with her family close behind her. "Hi, I'm Dr. Manalis," I greet the three of them. Some parents enter my office and shake my hand, but usually the parents of young children do not. All of the energy and attention of such parents is focused on shepherding their offspring into the office and hoping the child does not kick or spit on the doctor. Some parents want the child on her best behavior with me. On the other hand, some parents are pleased when their child acts up at the doctor visit, because this demonstrates the problem. It's similar to wanting your car engine to malfunction for the mechanic just as it did for you on the interstate two days before you brought it into the repair shop.

As for my diagnostic needs, I like to see the child at both her best and worst behaviors during the interview. The good behaviors give me a sense of the child's self-control skills and the worst behaviors give me a dose of empathy for the exhausted and perplexed parents and help me in making a diagnosis.

"Sarah, please sit in this chair between your mother and grandmother," I direct her, testing her receptive language skills and her willingness to cooperate. Sarah is a cute girl, her hair in rows of tight braids, clipped to her scalp with small pink barrettes that match her pink shirt with its scalloped sleeves and her blue jeans with pink flowers on the pockets. How did they get her to sit long enough for this stylish dressing, I wonder? She is unable to stay in the chair I have directed her to and instead stands before my bookshelf, looking at my toys. Instead of picking up a toy and playing with it, she surprises me by loudly dropping onto the floor, one by one, the wooden puzzles, then the books, and, finally, a large blue truck.

"Sarah, sit in the chair like the doctor asked you to," her mother pleads again.

"No!" Sarah emphatically replies.

"This is part of the problem," her mother tells me. "She is very defiant. She says 'no' all the time. She hits me and her grandmother and her playmates.

Last week at the doctor's office, the doctor knelt down to her level to say hello and Sarah hit the doctor in the face! I was really embarrassed. At home, I use time outs and spankings, but they don't faze her."

"I am glad you are using time outs. I don't recommend spankings. We can talk later about how to make the time outs more effective," I respond.

When interviewing the adults about a child, I ask each family member present for his or her unique view of the child. A variety of adult views can be an unexpected eye opener for me in understanding the child. Today I seek the grandmother's observations. "I agree with Sarah's mom, plus she is hyperactive just like my son, her dad, was at this age. She's a spitting image of her dad. He took Ritalin as a child and had trouble learning."

"This is important information since we know that Attention Deficit Hyperactivity Disorder can be passed in the parent's genes to the child," I respond. Turning to Sarah's mother I ask, "Is Sarah in preschool yet?"

"No, but I want to get her in soon," her mother replies.

"I am glad to hear Sarah will be starting preschool, since studies show that preschool programs for three- and four-year-olds are helpful in preparing them for kindergarten. It can improve her social skills and her learning skills. Once she has attended preschool for two or three weeks, I want the teacher's observations of her behaviors on this checklist I will give you: can she focus during activities, can she remain seated, is she hitting her classmates or teacher? Can she cooperate and be redirected?"

As I continue to gather information about Sarah's history, I learn that her mother smoked during the pregnancy, thereby doubling the odds for Sarah to have Attention Deficit Hyperactivity Disorder. Her father's ADHD adds a possible genetic risk.

In her first year of life, Sarah was colicky, hard to comfort, and a poor sleeper. But now she sleeps the recommended ten hours a night. Adequate sleep helps a young child with self-control. Sarah began walking, talking, and toilet training ahead of schedule. Fortunately, and I always breath a big sigh of relief on this one, Sarah has not experienced neglect of her need for food or shelter, nor has she been physically or sexually abused. This good fortune makes Sarah's improvement more likely and my work much easier.

To myself during the interview, I weigh Sarah's positive attributes. She has excellent language skills, using complex sentences instead of just three- word sentences. While showing me a handful of small red plastic monkeys from my bookshelf, she asks me, "How do you do this?" Her articulation is perfect. Many of the three-year-olds I see have some trouble clearly articulating letters like "r" and "t," which can make it difficult for adults and playmates to understand them.

But Sarah's development is above average in several areas. Parents sometimes find that a child's high intelligence makes discipline a particular challenge. A bright child may succeed in out-manipulating her parents.

On the negative side, I note that my attempt to redirect Sarah to sit in a chair has failed; as I ask her mother for information, Sarah intrudes by talking loudly and yelling, even when she is not angry or upset. Is she trying to get attention? I'm not yet sure of the why of this and I don't want to jump to a conclusion that might be wrong, so I'll keep an open mind about the cause. She can't sit in the chair for more than two seconds. Her "no" conveys a stubborn temperament.

"Let's review how I understand Sarah's problem behaviors," I say, turning to mother and grandmother again. Sarah may have ADHD like her father did as a child. But I prefer to wait until she is in preschool next month to get her teacher's observations of her before I make this diagnosis.

"While you are arranging for the preschool program, I want Sarah and both of you and Sarah's dad to work with one of our counselors. The counselor will help you improve your discipline and parenting skills. She will also use play therapy to help Sarah learn to identify and express her feelings in words instead of acting them out by hitting and throwing things. Sarah's use of words is above average and this will give her an advantage in learning to express her feelings verbally.

"When we meet again in four weeks I will have the teacher's input and can decide about Sarah's diagnosis and whether medication will help her. You will have worked on discipline and Sarah will be learning to verbalize her anger instead of hitting people."

Sarah's mother and grandmother agree to this plan.

I turn to Sarah, "It is time to say goodbye, Sarah, but first I want you to put the toys back on the bookshelf." I request this of each child for several reasons: first, to assess how compliant the child is with this simple request; second to see whether she can organize the toys on the shelf; and lastly because I don't like cleaning up someone else's mess. Sarah ignores my request. "If you want to play with my toys the next time you come to see me, you need to put them on the shelf." Sarah again ignores me and continues playing. Her mother, embarrassed, begins to pick the toys up for her. "I see you are cleaning up for Sarah. My rule is since she played with the toys, she must put them away." By then her mother has them put away.

"See you all in four weeks. Goodbye."

"Goodbye," I hear from Sarah's mother and grandmother, as Sarah prances out of the room and down the hallway ahead of them.

· · · · · · · ● · · · · · · · · · ·

It is four weeks later, and Sarah has started preschool. Her teacher has completed my behavior checklist and indicates Sarah has low focus, and is hyperactive, easily distracted, and impulsive. Sarah's mother agreed two weeks ago when I called her about the teacher's observations, to start Sarah on a small dose of short-acting stimulant each morning to cover her three hours in preschool. Upon Sarah's starting this, the teacher reports an immediate improvement in all of Sarah's ADHD symptoms. Sarah's family is having better success with discipline and Sarah is more cooperative with her parents. When I see her at this visit, her hyperactivity and focus are greatly improved. So I decide to let her play with the toys, sensing she will clean them up this time. And she does. We also decide to add a noon dose of stimulant to cover the afternoons when she is at home.

· · · · · · · ● · · · · · · · · · ·

At our every three month appointments, I check Sarah's height and weight, as stimulants often reduce a child's appetite and can interfere with growth. When Sarah gains less than a pound a month, I suggest supplemental calories at breakfast, snack time, and bedtime to help growth. Sarah's social and learning skills are improving and she should be ready for kindergarten in two years.

The Girl with ADHD and PTSD Whose Adoption Rescued Her

Five-year-old Katie is brought to see me today by Mr. and Mrs. Henry, her foster mother and father. Katie is as cute as a sandy-haired puppy, with blond hair in soft curls, held back by red bow clips on each side. She's wearing a blue summer pinafore and white sandals. I rarely see girls in skirts or dresses these days. Even though her foster mother has dressed her with obvious care, the flat look on Katie's face betrays the sad life she has experienced in her five short years — neglect and possible physical and sexual abuse, resulting in removal from her parents when she was three. After one year at a different foster home, Katie and her six-year-old half-sister, Molly, are in a stable home with the Henrys who hope to adopt them both if their biological parents' rights are terminated by the court. For now, the girls have supervised visits with their birth parents.

Mr. Henry is a tall, handsome man with dark hair and a stiff, military stance, but he softens his demeanor with a warm smile. Mrs. Henry is a stately woman who conveys a sense of knowing how to raise children even though she and her husband, in their forties now, have no biological children. This is their first try at parenting, and Katie and Molly come to them not as infants whom they can mold, but as wounded and emotionally scarred children with difficult behaviors. Mr. and Mrs. Henry are committed to this venture of adopting and raising Katie and Molly, and seem confident that a loving home will heal their wounds and return them to a normal path of development.

The girls have been rescued by the government agency whose mission it is to protect children from abuse and neglect. Will Katie's first three years of life with her birth parents — lacking food, not being held and comforted as an infant, and likely experiencing sexual and physical abuse— prove to haunt her and her sister forever? Or will this nurturing home, along with mental health services, be a healing balm? Time will tell. The girls are fortunate there are people like the Henrys, willing to take on the commitment as well as the risks involved. The Henrys have been warned by the adoption agency that it could be rough going. Agencies seem to me to be more open with adoptive parents about a child's traumatic history than they were in past years when often it was kept hidden.

Today the concern is with Katie's behaviors: hyperactivity and short attention span at home and school, poor progress in learning at school. Her temper tantrums were a problem, but these have improved this year, as she has lived with the Henrys. Her sleep has improved also, but still is less than the nine hours each night recommended for a child her age. She knows more than a child should about sex: "She told me how French kissing is done," Mrs. Henry shares with me at our first interview. Katie's counselor has been working with her in play therapy on her Posttraumatic Stress Disorder from the abuse and neglect during her first three years of life.

· · · · · · · · · ● · · · · · · · · · · ·

Four years have passed since I began working with Katie, and she has made good progress. The Henrys were able to adopt Katie and her sister, changing their last name to Henry.

I diagnosed Katie with Attention Deficit Hyperactivity Disorder, and after trying a number of different stimulant medications, one was found that had minimal side effects and helped her focus improve. The school tested her and found she qualified for special education because of a delay in reading. In addition to the school's extra help, the Henrys hired a private tutor for her. In third grade, Katie's reading level was a year behind her grade level, so Mrs. Henry decided to have her repeat third grade, even though the school did not recommend it. By the time she enters fourth grade at age nine, her reading skills have caught up. Katie has continued in play therapy these four yeas with her counselor, resulting in gradual improvement of her Posttraumatic Stress Disorder symptoms.

A stable home, plus school and mental health interventions, have healed some of the delays and wounds Katie had. Thank you, adoptive parents, for all your good deeds, and for being willing to take the risks involved in healing children who have had difficult beginnings. The factors most predictive of good outcomes for children like Katie and Molly: committed, loving parents who have made themselves knowledgeable of the effects of trauma on a child's development; a school system providing extra help, and mental health services with professionals trained in treating children with PTSD and ADHD.

The Boy with Attention Deficit Hyperactivity Disorder

I see lots of children with Attention Deficit Hyperactivity Disorder (ADHD) in my psychiatric practice. A government research group called The National Institute of Mental Health reported in 2006 that about four out of one hundred American children have ADHD. An organization representing American child psychiatrists, The American Academy of Child and Adolescent Psychiatry, reported in 2007 that seven out of one hundred American children have ADHD, more frequently affecting boys than girls. In a classroom of twenty children, on average, one student will have ADHD. It is estimated that eighty out of one hundred children with ADHD have inherited this neurobiological disorder. Other causes of ADHD may be the child's mother smoking, using alcohol, or being exposed to lead during the pregnancy (www.medscape.com/viewarticle/546469_2).

For most of my patients with ADHD, my help in making a diagnosis and in treatment with medications makes a dramatic improvement in the child's ability to focus and to learn. So, I feel a sense of satisfaction in what sometimes seems like a miraculous change. Here is the story of seven-year-old John: I welcome John and his father into my office today. I am glad to see an involved father, because, sadly, I don't see many fathers in my work with children. I always invite each father to be part of his child's appointments with me, but often the father lives apart from the child, with weekend visitation, or the father may be completely absent from his child's life or he may be out of the country fighting the war in Iraq or he may be in jail. But here is John's father, a small, wiry man, dressed in jeans, bringing his son to see me for a psychiatric evaluation. John is a small, thin boy with an anxious look on his face as he huddles close to his father. Mr. Graham smiles at John, trying to make him feel unafraid of this new doctor. He speaks softly as he tells me what concerns he has about John.

"He's having temper tantrums. I use time outs and take away privileges as punishment. I try not to spank him. His first-grade teacher tells me John can't sit still in class or focus on his work, and his grades are all failing."

"Tell me about John's birth and preschool years," I say.

"When John's mother was pregnant, she smoked cigarettes and drank alcohol. I tried to get her to stop, but she refused. John was fussy as a baby and it was hard to get him to stop crying. I'm a recovering alcoholic and gave up drinking before John was born. But his mother was drunk a lot when John was little while I was at work. I knew this wasn't good, but I needed to keep working. John used to have bruises from his mother hitting him with a belt. His mother and I were fighting all the time, which upset the kids, so I left. I know leaving the kids was wrong, but I didn't know what else to do.

"Six months after I left, the kids called 911 because their mother was so drunk they couldn't wake her up. They thought she was dead. The court got involved and asked me to take all three kids, so I did. Things have been hard this last year, so I came here to your clinic to get help with my parenting and to get the kids some counseling and whatever treatment they need after all they have been through."

"It sounds like it has been a rough year for all of you. I'm glad you have sought help for your family. My role with John is to make a diagnosis and recommend medications if they are needed. Let's start by having you give John's teacher this ADHD checklist to complete and return to me so I can see if John has ADHD." (The Vanderbilt Parent and Teacher ADHD Symptom Lists and scoring directions are available free at www.psychiatrictimes.com).

"If John has ADHD I would like to try him on a type of medicine we call stimulants. Stimulants help increase focus and decrease hyperactivity, distractibility, and impulsivity. The downside to a stimulant medicine can include a decrease in appetite with weight loss, an increase in aggression and moodiness, and sometimes upset stomach, headaches, and tics. If there are heart problems in your family, please let me know before we start a stimulant. You should also ask the school to test John for learning disabilities or slow learning, since he is failing all his subjects."

"Ok. There aren't any heart problems I know of in our family," Mr. Graham replies.

"Good. Let's meet in a few weeks. When I get the ADHD checklist back from John's teacher, I will call you and discuss the results and advise whether we should start the stimulant."

"Ok."

· · · · · · · ● · · · · · · · · ·

It is a month later and I have started John on a low dose of short-acting stimulant after his teacher reported she observed fifteen out of the eighteen ADHD symptoms. I like to start on a low dose and watch for side effects, then gradually increase the dose to a level where the teacher notes improved focus and ability to sit still. Often after the dose is determined, I switch from the short-acting stimulant, given two to three times a day, to a long- acting one taken just once in the morning.

"How is John doing on his new medicine, Mr. Graham?" I ask at our follow up appointment.

"His teacher says he can sit still and focus now. The school tested him and told me that he is a slow learner and will struggle to get Cs, but he does not qualify for special education. His grades are beginning to improve since we started the medicine," Mr. Graham reports.

"John, let's get your weight today. Good. You have gained a pound in the last month. We can switch to the once-a-day long-acting medicine now. John may not feel hungry at lunch or dinner. Try to get calories in him at breakfast and bedtime, when the medicine is gone from his system. Protein foods like peanut butter, yogurt, and cheese, as well as protein shakes that are approved for children can help him continue to gain weight."

"Ok. The once-a-day medicine will be more convenient for me. John is still stubborn with me at home and talks back to me," Mr. Graham reports.

"The ADHD medicine does not help with defiant behavior. The defiance needs to be worked on in his counseling. Bringing John to counseling weekly will provide a safe place for him to work on his anger and his sadness about missing his mother, improve his social skills with other children, and talk about the traumatic events from his past. The counselor can help you tune into John's emotional life and help you with your discipline skills."

"Ok. I will make sure he and I see his counselor each week."

"Good. John, I am glad you are doing better in school. I notice that you suck your thumb a lot while you are here."

"Yes," John replies, "I suck it all the time."

Turning to John's father I reflect, "Thumb sucking means a child feels fearful and insecure, so this is another way his counselor can help."

· · · · · · ● · · · · · · · · ·

It is a year since I first met John, who is eight years old now, and his father.

Over this past year, I have been seeing them every three months to review John's medication, his progress, and his growth.

"Hi, John and Mr. Graham. How is John doing in school?"

"He's in second grade and getting mostly Bs and Cs. He still has trouble with spelling and has a D. The school is giving him speech therapy and they say he is improving. I'm giving him extra snacks at breakfast and at bedtime, like you suggested. He does his chores at home better and doesn't talk back to me as much as he used to. I think seeing his counselor each week is helping him." Mr. Graham shares.

"Ok, that sounds wonderful, John. Let's check your weight. Good, you gained three pounds in the last three months. I see you are not sucking your thumb now. That's good too."

"I only suck it at home, not at school anymore," John says.

"Are you feeling less worried now?" I ask.

"Yes, but I still miss my mom. I do get to talk to her on the phone," John reports.

· · · · · · ● · · · · · · · · ·

It's two years since I first met John and he is nine years old now and in third grade. He is on a long-acting stimulant whose dose I increased a month ago because his teacher noticed some decrease in his focus and an increase in his hyperactivity. Mr. Graham has continued to give John protein snacks, but today his weight has dropped by two pounds, likely from the increased dose of his medicine a month ago.

"Hi, John. Mr. Graham, how is John doing in school and at home?"

"Well he is getting some As and some Fs. He isn't eating as well and he is more defiant with me about doing his chores," Mr. Graham says.

"The school may need to provide special services for John. Some children qualify for special services at school based on having ADHD. I know the school said their testing did not meet the criteria for special education, but I suggest you challenge the school about this idea. Here is the phone number of an advocacy agency who can help you talk to the school about this.

"Regarding John's defiance with you about doing his chores, today I talked to John's counselor and she is planning to set up a reward system you can use at home where John can earn points towards a reward if he does his chores. We know that when good behavior is rewarded, a child is more likely to continue the good behavior. Rewards can be stars on a chart placed on the refrigerator for all to see, praise from a parent, special time with a parent, or a treat or small toy.

"Next let's work on John's weight, so he gains a pound a month. Perhaps adding a child's protein shake in the mornings to the protein snacks you are giving him at bedtime will help him gain. Skipping the medicine on weekends and during school breaks can help too," I suggest.

My work with John and his father end, as the family doctor takes over management of the ADHD medications. John will need to continue on a stimulant at least through his adolescence and perhaps into adulthood. This has been a rewarding family to work with.

CHAPTER FIVE

Childhood Depression

THIS CHAPTER WILL introduce you to the symptoms of childhood depression and to three children and one teenager whom I helped.

Symptoms of Depression

- Sad or irritable mood most of each day. Crying or snapping in anger daily.
- Loss of interest in most activities previously enjoyed.
- Lack of appetite resulting in unintentional weight loss or increased appetite with weight gain.
- Sleeping too many hours (over nine hours a night) or too few hours (less than eight for children and teens).
- Little energy most days.
- Activity level is much slower than usual or much greater than usual (agitation).
- Feeling worthless most of the time.
- Feeling overly sensitive to rejection by others or to criticism from others.
- Feeling excessive and constant guilt over small things.
- Poor concentration with falling grades in school.
- Loss of interest in schoolwork or job.
- Thoughts of death bringing relief.

- Making verbal threats to family or friends of wanting to be dead.
- Thoughts of killing oneself, but without a plan.
- Thoughts of suicide with a plan for committing suicide.
- Gathering objects to carry out a plan for suicide.
- Psychotic symptoms can be present, such as hearing voices (hallucinations).
- Depression must last for at least a two-week period or more.

Adapted from DSM-5

The Boy with Sadness

Jack is almost eight years old. He lives with two sisters, his mother, and her boyfriend. He has not seen his dad for the last three years. Jack has been working with a counselor each week for two months, but the counselor noted he is shut down and guarded with her, making it difficult to make progress. She referred him to me for consideration of medication for his depression.

As Jack and his mother enter my office today, I notice that the red shirt Jack is wearing is printed with "I didn't do it!" I have the fantasy that kids' t-shirts, with their pictures of skulls, race cars, motorcycles, Disney characters and pithy statements tell me something about each kid. I see so many kids who are misbehaving at home and at school that a mantra of "I didn't do it" would fit many of them. Jack's khaki pants and his taupe slip-on shoes tell me that he is into the latest styles and that he is probably middle-class, as he is able to afford a cutting-edge outfit.

Jack's mother, Mrs. Green, is pleasant-looking in her stylish slacks and blouse. She shares her concerns about Jack, as he sits passively next to her. "He hates losing at games and will run out of the house or scream and throw things when he is mad. Recently, he got into a fistfight with a neighbor kid. He has been aggressive since he was five, the year his father moved out of state. Over the last six months, Jack looks sad to me. He keeps to himself and he sleeps twelve hours every night and is still tired."

Today Jack wears a sad look on his face, but doesn't cry during the interview. I note he is very guarded and answers in single words or a nod of his head. When I ask him whether he was touched in his privates or hit by an adult leaving a bruise on him, he replies no. He seems to have escaped any physical or sexual abuse. Why do I accept the validity of his response? I have found over the years of asking this question, that most children are amazingly open with me when I ask them about being abused. In addition, I corroborate the child's response with the parents' awareness of this area.

Mrs. Green adds, "But when Jack was three, his dad pushed me into a window and it broke. When Jack was five, his dad tried to push me out of the car. Then he would call on the phone to threaten me, so I got a restraining order. Things have been better these last three years with Jack's dad out of our lives."

"Jack, do you remember any of the fights between your mother and dad?" I ask.

"I remember when dad pushed mom into a window and the glass broke all over the floor. I thought he was trying to kill mom. I was scared," Jack answers.

"Age three is the earliest most kids remember events, and Jack has remembered the glass breaking and his fear. We know when children witness domestic violence it can be emotionally traumatizing to them," I explain.

"Do you miss your dad, Jack?" I ask.

"Sometimes I'm sad. But mostly I'm mad that mom split up with dad."

"What do you wish for most in your life, Jack?" I ask.

"I wish I didn't get mad so much and I wish my dad would come back and live with me and mom."

"Do you ever wish you were dead, Jack?"

"Sometimes I do, but I never tried anything."

Turning to Mrs. Green I suggest, "I recommend an antidepressant to help Jack with his sadness and his low energy. His tiredness may be caused by a medical problem like anemia, so I may send him to his family doctor if he doesn't perk up with an antidepressant. Be aware of a possible side effect of suicidal ideas developing in children on antidepressants. Jack already has suicidal ideas. But Jack, if you think more often about wanting to die, tell your mother right away so she can call me. A decrease in thoughts of suicide should occur instead of an increase over the next two to four weeks.

So I will see you both back in four weeks."

• • • • • • • • ● • • • • • • • • •

It's four weeks later and Jack enters my office smiling. "How is your sadness, Jack?' I ask.

"I feel mad less now and I'm not tired like I was," Jack says.

"I agree with Jack. He smiles more and doesn't get frustrated and mad so easily," Mrs. Green says.

"Jack, are you having any thoughts about wishing you were dead?" I ask.

"Not the last couple of weeks," Jack answers.

"It takes the antidepressant medicine two to four weeks to work, so it looks like it is helping. Jack, have you heard from your dad?" I ask.

"No, and I do wish he would call me," Jack says.

"Reconnecting with his Dad is a wish Jack has, and one you could facilitate, Mrs. Green, if you know how to contact him. I know this may be uncomfortable for you because of the past domestic violence you experienced, but it could be helpful to Jack," I suggest.

"I will see if I can locate your Dad, Jack," Mrs. Green replies.

Jack's wish has been heard by me and his mother. And so life moves on.

Silence Takes Its Toll

Children are usually bubbling with laughter, calling to each other as they go about their play. On the playground, they squeal with glee as they whoosh down the slide. We don't think of children becoming deeply depressed. We expect a few tears shed over something they want but can't have — a brief sadness. But contrary to our thinking, mental health research tells us that some children do become seriously depressed. This is a story about a ten-year-old girl whose sadness has turned into a deep depression.

Ann is a cute, stylish girl with curly brown hair, a sad look on her face, and a slump in her shoulders. She is wearing a colorful outfit of purple slacks, a red sweater, and black, shiny knee-high boots. As I invite Ann and her mother into my office and they are seated, I explain: "Ann, I'm going to ask your mother a lot of questions, so you can sit back and relax until later, when I will ask you some questions."

She sits back in her chair and listens quietly as her mother explains her concerns to me. "Ann is a good girl and a top student. But her teachers as well as her father and I notice that she looks sad. At home she stays in her room a lot and when she does come out, she blows up over small things. Her feelings are easily hurt. Sometimes she even bites her arms and pulls her hair out when she's mad," Mrs. Jones shares wearily. Two years of this is a long time, I think to myself, both for Ann to suffer and for her family to endure her irritability and isolation.

"Were there any deaths or illnesses or divorces two years ago, when her sadness started?" I ask Ann's mother, a pleasant-looking woman with short blond hair, gray slacks, and a striped red blouse. "Depression in children is usually set off by a loss of some kind."

"Two years ago we had a new baby. Also that year, Ann's great aunt died, but she was not close to her since she lived far away. In spite of these changes, I feel our family has been doing well."

"Does depression run in your family or in Ann's father's family?" I ask. "Yes, we have depressed relatives on both sides," Mrs. Jones responds. "Some depressions have a genetic component and run in families, so this family history raises Ann's risk for depression. Let me ask Ann about her feelings to determine if this is a depression and to see what events may have started her problems. Ann, have you been feeling sad?" I inquire.

"I'm just mad a lot of the time. Sometimes I start crying and I can't stop."

"Ann, do you feel you are good at anything?" I ask. "Not really," Ann replies sadly.

"What things do you like to do for fun?" I ask.

"I used to like to read and draw, but now I'm mostly bored. I just don't have much interest once I get my school work done," Ann shares.

"Does it take very long for you to fall asleep?" I ask.

"Yes, some nights it takes a long time for me to fall asleep, then I'm tired all day," Ann reports.

"It sounds like you have what we call depression. How long do you think you have felt this sad?" I inquire.

"A long time," Ann slowly responds.

"Do you ever wish you were dead?" I ask.

"No, I don't feel that way, but I do feel like I'm a bad person, like I've done something bad," Ann confides.

"I need to ask you some difficult questions that may make you uncomfortable. but they are important ones for me to better understand your feelings: Has anyone touched your private area?" I am looking for a stress that Ann experienced which her family may not know about.

Ann hesitates then quickly looks away. Turning back to me, she blurts out, "Yes!"

"Can you tell me who touched your privates?" I ask in a calm voice.

"My best friend. Mom let me sleep at her house a lot when I was eight, because my Mom and Dad worked at their jobs at night. I'm not allowed to sleep at her house anymore. Now, every night when I try to fall asleep, I think about how she touched me when I slept in bed with her. I feel like I did something wrong, like it was my fault that it happened. I feel dirty even after I take a shower. I just can't feel clean any more," Ann shares.

After Ann's revelation to me, I turn to Mrs. Jones and ask, "Were you aware of this?"

"Yes. Ann told us about it last year. By then it had been going on for several months. We stopped letting her sleep at her friend's house as soon as we learned about it."

"Did you report it to Children's Protective Services or to the police?"

"No, we didn't report it to the police; we just made sure it stopped," Mrs. Jones replies.

"I am required by law to report suspected child abuse to Children's Protective Services (CPS). Their staff will interview Ann and her friend separately and determine what happened." Mrs. Jones, unlike some parents in this uncomfortable situation, does not protest my plan to report the suspected abuse to CPS. The child abuse law requires that not just doctors, but any adult who suspects a child is being neglected or physically or sexually abused, must report this information to the police or to CPS. I believe this law has helped prevent some persons who molest children from harming new victims. In addition, both the child victim and the molester benefit when the legal system does its job correctly and the court and mental health systems become involved.

Some families I have worked with have been permanently fractured when the secret of molestation comes out into the open. Some mothers have taken the side of their abusive husbands or boyfriends instead of being supportive and protective of a victim daughter or son. This tragedy upon tragedy happens all too often. The victim may then need to enter foster care or go live with another relative who can keep him or her safe.

Fortunately, most parents take action to keep a child safe, and immediately break off contact with the molesting spouse, relative, or neighbor. These protective and supportive parents are enormously helpful to the abused child on his or her journey of healing from the abuse.

At the end of my first session with Ann and her mother, I diagnose both Depression and Posttraumatic Stress Disorder. I recommend three parts for Ann's treatment: first, that she see a counselor to help her work on her depression and her disturbing memories of the sexual involvement with her friend; second, that Ann take an antidepressant medicine to help with her depression and her feelings about her traumatic experience; third, I explain that she and her friend will each be interviewed separately by a person from

Children's Protective Services about what happened between them, and that person will develop a plan to help both Ann and her friend.

· · · · · · •••• ● •••• · · · · · ·

When I meet with Ann and her mother four weeks later, Ann's mood seems much brighter. She has been seeing her counselor each week and taking her antidepressant medicine. Her depression has lessened. She is no longer blaming herself for being molested, and the memories of the sexual touches have decreased from daily to once a week.

Children's Protective Services has interviewed both Ann and her friend. Ann's parents are told by CPS that Ann is not to be alone with this friend, nor to sleep over at her friend's house. Ann feels comfortable with these rules, which are the same ones her parents' instituted. CPS has recommended mental health services for Ann's friend and has placed her on probation through the Juvenile Justice System. Ann is glad her friend will get some help from a counselor.

So, Ann's sadness, and the irritability that her parents noticed over a two-year period, appear to have grown out of her experience of being molested. Her guilt and shame about the experience with her best friend festered. The family assumed that removing Ann from contact with the friend resolved the situation, and they shut the door on the experience. However, Ann's sense of sadness, shame and guilt continued to grow in the silence that ensued. Once she was able to talk to the counselor and me about the events, she began to heal. Keeping silent about stressful events takes its toll.

I want to explain my interview style with Ann. I was very direct in asking her about sexual experiences. Some of my readers may feel I was too abrupt and insensitive. However, I ask you to consider whether there is a delicate way to ask about this area. I have not found one. I try to be gentle by warning a child I will be asking some questions that may make him or her uncomfortable. The many preteen children I have worked with over the years do not seem offended by my directness. Most do not even appear embarrassed about sexual questions, as teens and adults often are; children are relieved to have their experiences heard and out in the open.

Why do I interview a child in the presence of parents? If the child has been abused, I want the parents to know this directly from the child, so they can see the distress in the child's face and hear the child's anxious words, and can take actions, both in reporting the abuse and in supporting the child during this difficult time.

Some people believe that sexual touching between same-aged children is normal. But in Ann's situation, her interaction with her friend over several months went beyond any normal sexual experimentation, causing Ann extreme emotional distress. Minimizing the significance of such sexual experiences between children is a mistake, I believe. For further discussion about the difference between normal sexual exploration in children and abusive sexual experiences, go to my chapter on Posttraumatic Stress Disorder. Also refer to the website www.stopitnow.org for helpful information.

The Girl Who Stopped Smiling

I marvel at the amount of stress children can manage until, finally, they just can't take another drop of it. Then they may lose interest in schoolwork and friends, become irritable with family, and even experience thoughts of wishing they were dead. At this point, parents come to see me, desperate for help. This is the story of such a girl. Her name is Sandra and she is fourteen.

Today, at my first session with Sandra and her mother, I see Sandra is an attractive teenager with short, dark, curly hair. She is wearing jeans with intentional rips at the knees and a t-shirt with a rock group pictured on the front. Her stylish dress tells me she still maintains an interest in how she looks. But she has a bland look on her face and is slumped in her chair, looking tired and discouraged. Her mother walks in slowly behind her, using a cane. I know from Bob, Sandra's counselor, that Mrs. Smith has multiple sclerosis, but I didn't know until I see her with her cane and listen to her difficulty in speaking that the disease had reached this disabling stage.

Bob has shared with me his work with Sandra of the past two months. He told me Sandra had been very depressed when he first met her. She had thoughts about killing herself and had cut her wrist the week before her mother brought her into our clinic. Sandra had given up on life and felt death would be an escape from the many stresses in her life. Bob helped her talk about the sadness that resulted from several recent deaths in her family, and about her anger over her mother's multiple sclerosis. Sandra is developing improved coping skills such as talking about her sad and angry feelings, and becoming assertive with kids who tease her at school. Her depression is better now, but Bob still feels she might benefit from an antidepressant medication.

Once Sandra and her mother are seated across from me, I introduce myself and explain the order of my interview: "Sandra, I would like to ask your mother some questions about you first, then a little later I will ask you some questions.

"Mrs. Smith, what is your main concern about Sandra?"

Mrs. Smith speaks haltingly as she describes Sandra's problems. "Sandra cries a lot these last few months. Her grades have dropped and she never calls her friends like she used to. Before that, Sandra was a cheerful girl who smiled. But she's had a lot of stress. Last year her grandfather and grandmother died. She was very close to both of them. Sandra watched them suffer through their painful deaths from cancer. I have multiple sclerosis and it is getting worse. Sandra's dad died when she was five from a heart attack, so I'm all she's got left besides her sister. I depend on Sandra and her sister to keep the house clean and our big yard mowed. I just can't do those things any more."

I turn to Sandra, knowing how children who have lost one parent worry about who will take care of them if they lose the remaining parent, "Who will take care of you, Sandra, if your mother is unable to?"

Sandra's mother abruptly answers for Sandra: "We have a back-up plan. She'll go live with my sister." I take note of Mrs. Smith's cutting off Sandra's response, but I must respect Mrs. Smith's focus of concern at this getting-acquainted stage, in order to build an alliance with her. If I recommend medications for Sandra, her mother must feel trust in me, and feel understood by me, if she is to take my suggestions.

Sandra's mother returns to her more immediate concern. "Sandra has a very bad temper, just like her father had. He was diagnosed with Bipolar, but the many medications he took never calmed his anger down. In his angry fits, he'd hit me while Sandra watched the whole thing. Now Sandra acts just like him by hitting the walls, throwing things, and breaking things when I ask her to do something simple, like the dishes. Last year, she got suspended from school for fighting with a girl. Her anger reminds me so much of her father's bad temper and it scares me."

I respond, gently changing the focus away from Sandra's anger to her sadness. I want to role model for Mrs. Smith how to delve into her daughter's hidden feelings. "Sometimes anger in a teen results from him or her being depressed. Let me ask Sandra about this. Sandra, how often do you feel sad and hopeless?"

"All the time," she answers mournfully. "I'm scared that Mom will die like my dad and grandparents did, and leave me all alone. I don't get to do things with my friends because I'm always cooking and doing dishes at home. There's no end to the cleaning and mowing. Mom used to do all those things, but now she can't."

"Sandra, does your sadness ever get so deep that you think about killing yourself?"

"Yes. Sometimes I think that death would be a way to find some peace."

It still amazes me how open children and teens are with me about their thoughts of suicide. Rarely does one even hesitate when I ask about such intentions, as if they feel lonely with these thoughts and want someone to inquire. I encourage parents to ask a depressed child about suicidal thoughts so the parents know if the thoughts are present. Many parents have the mistaken idea that asking about suicide will put that thought into a child's mind. Perhaps this confusion comes from media examples of the contagion phenomenon: teens copying friends who attempt or complete suicide. This certainly happens. But asking your child or teen calmly "Are you having thoughts about killing yourself?" can save a life.

Sometimes parents will hear a child or teen threaten suicide when the child is angry. Then parents may disregard the threat as a manipulation by the child to get what she wants. However, a threat, even one made in anger, should be taken seriously and professional help sought immediately A threat of suicide is a child's way of expressing how desperate she feels.

Sandra's mother, following my lead to explore Sandra's sadness and desperation, shares: "A few months ago Sandra told me she wanted to be dead, and a few days after that, when she was visiting her girlfriend, Sandra cut her wrist with a razor."

"Can I see where you cut yourself, Sandra?" I ask, bending toward her. I look at the scar as she reluctantly stretches her arm towards me. I see a thin, two-inch scar that appears to be from a shallow cut. It is not located over the artery of her wrist. "Did you want to be dead when you cut your wrist, Sandra?"

"No, I didn't want to be dead. I just felt like giving up, like life isn't fair. I miss my dad and grandparents. I wish Mom could take care of me like she used to."

"You have much to be sad about, Sandra," I respond softly. "Do you have a plan of how you'd kill yourself?"

"No, I don't. I just feel things will never get better."

"Sandra, your ability to share your feelings will help in healing from your depression as you work with your counselor. Are you finding your work with Bob helpful?"

"Yes, I really like talking to Bob. He seems to understand me, but I'm still mad all the time."

"Depressed people often lose the ability to be patient, so they snap at minor things instead of being able to let the small stuff roll off them. I suspect that your anger problem is part of your depression and not related to the anger problem your father had."

I turn to Sandra's mother. "Because Sandra's depression is still strong, even with the counseling, I am recommending that in addition to her counseling, she take an antidepressant." We discuss the benefits and side effects of the antidepressant I like to use with teens. It is a long-acting one that will continue to work if the teen occasionally forgets to take it, which in my experience with teens often happens. A safety feature is that it is not lethal if taken in overdose. I also discuss with Sandra and her mother a recent warning the Federal Drug Administration has added to antidepressants used in children and teens: that some antidepressants may bring on thoughts of suicide. In Sandra's case, she is already having thoughts of suicide. If these thoughts become stronger, Sandra and her mother are to notify me immediately. (For further information on side effects of antidepressants, see www.nimh.nih.gov and search under side effects of antidepressants).

"Yes, let's give it a try," Sandra's mother says as Sandra nods her head in agreement.

"Be patient, because it takes two to four weeks to see improvement. See your therapist weekly and see me again in four weeks."

Sandra manages a small smile as she and her mother leave the office, her mother tagging behind with her slow, unsteady gait.

· · · · · · · · · ● · · · · · · · · · · ·

It's three months later when Sandra comes to a second appointment with me. She was to return in four weeks for me to review how her antidepressant was working and to adjust the dose or change to a different medication if she was not better. I'm concerned, since her depression three months ago was in the moderate-to-severe range.

It is the mother's responsibility to bring Sandra to see me regularly. If she can't bring her, then she must ask someone else to bring Sandra. Good compliance, that is, doing what the doctor recommends, often determines whether emotional problems will improve. Parents must not only advocate for a child with emotional problems, but must also follow through with the treatment plan.

As Sandra walks into my office, I am relieved that an adult has taken on the responsibility of bringing her to see me, and that she has a smile on her face. Her grandmother on her father's side, to whom she is very close, has brought her today, because Sandra's mother's multiple sclerosis is worsening.

"Sandra, how is your depression?" I ask, after introducing myself to her grandmother.

"It is so much better and I am controlling my anger better, too," Sandra smiles. "My grandma is helping me take care of Mom. My grades are better and Bob has taught me how to ignore kids teasing me at school."

"That's great, Sandra. Are you having any thoughts about suicide?"

"Not any more. Those have been gone for a couple of months, about a month after I started the medicine you gave me."

"She seems happier to me," Sandra's grandmother chimes in. "I was afraid Sandra had inherited her father's bad temper. But Sandra is back to her old self now and she doesn't fly off the handle as much. She has a lot on her shoulders with her mom's illness and now her sister isn't around to help. I'm giving Sandra help with her chores and I'm spending more time with her."

"I think your involvement has been one of the reasons Sandra's depression has improved. I am pleased with her improvement. Sandra, are you still seeing your counselor here at our clinic?"

"No, I haven't seen him for two months, since Mom has been worse and couldn't bring me."

"We know that the best way to improve your depression is a combination of an antidepressant along with counseling. Mrs. Jones, can you bring Sandra to see her counselor each week as you brought her to see me today?"

"Yes, I will do that, now that I know how important it is for Sandra's depression. It is so good to see her smiling again!"

I review with Sandra and her grandmother the importance of Sandra staying on the antidepressant for at least six more months, and explain that I need to see her in three months.

· · · · · · · ● · · · · · · · ·

What does Sandra's future look like? I expect her depression will continue to improve when I see her in three months, and again three months after that. Then, since this is her first depression, she may be able to stop the antidepressant medication. She may go through life without depression returning. However, since she has some relatives with depression, she is genetically at risk for a return of depression. Only time will tell what her pattern will be.

If her depression returns, Sandra, her mother and her grandmother will feel comfortable in seeking help. They will see mental health services as safe and helpful, due to their success with this experience.

The Teen Who Overdosed

Nick is a sixteen-year-old who is short and stocky, with a pleasant demeanor. He is telling me today about the return of his depression. His mother and father, Mr. and Mrs. Samson, even though they have been divorced since Nick was five, have both come with him to his appointment. I am pleased they have accompanied him, as it provides me with more information, and likely makes Nick feel supported.

Before I share the details of Nick's life, I want to talk briefly about children of divorce. When I see a child of divorce, I like to have all parents, including step-parents, present at the first appointment in order to glean each one's view of the child's problem, to form an alliance with each parent, to gain some sense of the family dynamics the child is living with, and to explain, to all involved, the medication options and their side effects. Rarely is this ideal of mine met. Many of the children and teens I see have parents who are divorced and in discord with each other. Usually only the parent with whom the child lives the majority of the time will attend the first appointment.

Most children adapt to the divorce and remarriage of their parents amazingly well if the biological parents reach a harmonious level of communication regarding child support, visitation schedules, schools, medical care, and so on. That is a critical IF. Good communication with an ex-spouse around child issues is hard to achieve. The courts have helped set a less divisive tone by requiring mediation between parents. Even more helpful are courts who order parents to take classes to understand the effects of divorce and of parent conflict on the child. Can each parent let go of grudges against the ex-spouse for the sake of their children's mental health? Can he or she encourage the child's involvement with the other parent? Suffice it to say that Nick is lucky to have both parents in harmony and at his side today.

Now to return to Nick's description of his struggles with depression: "I first got depressed when I was twelve and had thoughts of wanting to be dead. I told my parents and they got treatment for me. I worked with a counselor and I took an antidepressant medicine which helped. I felt better after a few months, so I quit taking it and I did ok until last week. A few days ago I took an exam which, if I passed it, would allow me to take college classes while I am still in high school. I couldn't answer even half the questions, so I went home feeling like a failure. No one was at home. Death looked like a way out. I swallowed a whole bottle of aspirin. But within fifteen minutes I had changed my mind. I wanted to live, so I made myself throw up. Then I called a friend, but I didn't tell him about the overdose. About two hours later, mom came home from work and I told her what I had done. She took me to the ER where I spent the night."

"Are you glad you are alive now?" I ask.

"Yes I am," Nick replies. "I had never tried to kill myself before, even though I had thoughts about it when I was twelve. But this time the thoughts were so strong I couldn't resist them. I thought of death as an escape from feeling like a failure."

Nick's father, a tall, handsome man, speaks up after listening respectfully to Nick's story. "What bothers me most is that Nick didn't let any of us know his depression was coming back. In the past, he has let us know." Mr. Samson's caring tone is helpful to Nick in this difficult situation.

Nick's mother openly shares about herself, "I've been depressed and so are many of my relatives. Depression runs deep in our family. We have always taken Nick to a counselor and psychiatrist when he gets depressed."

"Has anyone in the family completed suicide?" I ask Mrs. Samson.

"No," she replies.

Nick has many relatives with depression, but, fortunately, no relative who has completed suicide. In addition, Nick's parents look for signs of depression, then seek appropriate help for him. Nick feels comfortable about telling his parents when he is depressed, instead of keeping such feelings a secret or telling only his friends, as some teens do. I turn to Nick and his parents: "It appears to me that Rick's recent suicidal thoughts came on so suddenly and intensely that he had no time to warn anyone of his returning depression."

Nick asks, "Can I return to the antidepressant I was on, but at a lower dose, so I don't feel groggy as I did before?"

"We can start at a lower dose, but may have to increase it, Nick. There is a new warning on all antidepressant medicines for teens that they may cause suicidal thoughts. You are already having these thoughts, Nick, but if they get more intense, let me know right away. It takes two to four weeks for the antidepressant to begin to improve your mood, so be patient. Once your depression improves, you will need to remain on the antidepressant for nine months, and perhaps longer, since you have had an earlier depression. See a counselor weekly to work on your sadness and worries. We know that the best treatment for depression is a combination of counseling and medication. I will see you and your parents in four weeks to check if the medicine is working."

· · · · · · · ● · · · · · · · · ·

It is a month later when Nick and his parents return. His depression has improved from severe to moderate and he has had no further thoughts of suicide. I suggest that we increase his antidepressant dose and Nick agrees to this. Over the following months, Nick continues his counseling and medication with good results. I alert him to not stop the antidepressant too soon, as there is a risk for a return of the depression if does so.

· · · · · · · ● · · · · · · · · ·

Following are some data about teen suicide (www.familyfirstaid.org, www.kidshealth.org, www.nimh.nih.gov/, www.aacap.org):

In America, suicide is the second-leading cause of death among 15- to 24-year-olds, following accidental deaths as a cause. In 2001, there were 272 suicide deaths among children ages ten to fourteen, and l,6ll suicide deaths among youth aged 15 to 19. The gender ratio for the 15- to 19-year-olds was five males to one female. Nearly 60 percent of completed suicides in the United States are committed with a gun. The risk of suicide increases when children and teens have access to guns at home. Girls attempt suicide most commonly by overdosing on drugs or by cutting their wrists. Boys more often use guns, or attempt hanging or jumping from heights, and are therefore more likely than are girls to succeed in killing themselves. One out of ten teens admits on surveys to thinking about suicide, and nearly half a million teens attempt suicide each year.

Teens confide in friends more often about suicidal ideas than they do their parents. The friend often feels that by holding this information in confidence, he is helping his friend. Nothing could be further from the truth. The friend needs to tell an adult who can seek professional help to save this child's life.

One school recently had two teens commit suicide in one year. In response, the school took action to prevent future suicides by making a depression screening program available to any high school student whose parents would give permission. The screening form is done by the student answering questions listed on a computer screen. Those teens identified as at risk for depression and suicide are referred to a counselor. This school has had no suicides since the program began a year ago.

Suicide hotlines have been saving lives for decades as mental health professionals and volunteers make themselves available by phone day and night in order to help save those on the verge of suicide. The American Foundation for Suicide Prevention (www. afsp.org) sponsors this service throughout America at 800-273-8255.

CHAPTER SIX

Childhood Bipolar Disorder

THIS CHAPTER WILL introduce you to the symptoms of childhood Bipolar Disorder and to one child and one teen with whom I worked.

Symptoms of Bipolar Disorder

Signs of mania or elevated moods:

- Feeling I'm on top of the world; I'm powerful and can do anything I want.
- I have lots of energy and never get tired.
- I don't need much sleep – maybe a couple of hours a night.
- I sometimes am awake for three days without sleep and don't feel tired.
- I get really mad over small things and yell at people.
- Sometimes I'm so mad I want to start fights.
- I feel restless often.
- I can't focus on anything for long.
- I spend money on things I can't afford.
- My friends tell me I talk really fast and loud.

Signs of depression or low moods:

- I feel very sad most of the time.
- I don't enjoy the things I used to, such as playing sports or reading.
- I sleep too much some nights and other nights I sleep very little.
- I often feel tired and hate getting out of bed in the morning.
- My appetite is huge sometimes and gone other times.
- My body hurts in lots of places, but the doctor finds nothing to cause this.
- I can't focus and I forget where I put things more than usual.
- I prefer to be alone and feel no one likes my company.
- I worry a lot and get mad often.
- I have thoughts about wanting to kill myself.

I go back and forth between feeling up and feeling down.

This page is adapted from the National Institutes of Health web page (www.nih.com). It can be given to a teenager as a checklist.

The Girl With Bipolar Disorder

If you Google "Bipolar Disorder in childhood" you will find psychiatrists emphasizing how commonly it occurs and lamenting how overlooked it is. I believe, to the contrary, that Bipolar Disorder is a much overused diagnosis in children. Bipolar Disorder is only to be given if there have been both periods of a manic mood and of a depressed mood. Most children only have the depressed mood and not the manic mood, thus making the diagnosis difficult until adolescence or adulthood when cycling between the mania and depression is seen. Because of these factors, I have been cautious while working with Sally to take time in determining her diagnosis. As I have come to know her over the months and years, I do believe she has Bipolar Disorder — with her irritability being the manic mood and her depression the depressed mood. Sally was six when I first met her and her mother, Mrs. Smith. Sally is fortunate to have a caring and perceptive mother and I am fortunate to be working with a patient's mother who is dependable in describing her child's symptoms and her changes in mood and behavior as we try various medications.

Sally's pediatrician was exceptionally observant in diagnosing her at the age of only four years with depression. He started her on a low dose of an antidepressant, but gradually increased it until she was on four times the usual adult dose. The pediatrician decided, after Sally had been on this high dose of an antidepressant medicine for two years, to lower the dose to see if it was still needed. This was a reasonable plan and I myself will sometimes take a child off a medicine to see if it is still helpful. Sally's depression, her anxiety, and her hand washing due to fear of germs all returned dramatically. At that point Mrs. Smith asked her pediatrician to refer Sally to a child psychiatrist.

Upon our first meeting, Mrs. Smith presented a long list of concerns: Sally's fearfulness about entering kindergarten; an increase in hand washing due to excessive fear of germs; Sally's irritability that was expressed in three or four daily temper tantrums at home, but not at school; and Sally's fear of storms. Even hearing the word "tornado" would make her anxious. Sally's dreams were often of tornados. At night her fears increased, causing her to be unable to sleep alone.

As Mrs. Smith described Sally's early years, I learned that the pregnancy and birth had been normal, and that as an infant Sally did not cry or fuss much, slept and ate well, and could be comforted by being held by her mother or father. As a toddler, she was referred for occupational therapy because of delays in both motor and sensory processing skills, but she eventually improved in these areas. In preschool she preferred to play alone. In kindergarten and first grade, while she learned well, she had trouble making friends. Further history indicated she had never been physically or sexually abused. Sally denied ever having hallucinations or thoughts of suicide or of homicide. The family history showed relatives with depression, anxiety, and bipolar disorder, as well as obsessive-compulsive problems and attention deficit hyperactivity disorder.

Neuropsychological testing done when she was six showed Sally's intelligence to be considerably above average, but her social and communication skills to be those of a four year old.

Sally has blonde, short hair and porcelain skin. Some days during our appointments she answers my questions, other days she hunches over in her chair with a scowl on her face and ignores me.

I have made changes to her medications over our months together with the goal of decreasing her irritability and temper tantrums. To her high dose of antidepressant medication, I added an antipsychotic medicine that served to decrease her irritability. Later, we try an anticonvulsant medicine that had helped a cousin with bipolar illness, and this medication helps Sally's irritability to further lessen. An anti-anxiety medicine is used to ease her anxiety in the transition from home to school when she is in first grade, but has not been needed in second or third grade. Sally sees a counselor weekly to work on emotional issues and this has been very helpful.

Below is a snapshot of several of our appointments over the past four years:

At age six: Sally sprawls across the chair opposite me, head turned away from me. She is irritable and screams when I ask about a nighttime dream: "I don't want to tell you about a dream!" Sally runs out of my office into the hallway, crying and screaming in frustration.

At age seven: As I add a mood stabilizing antipsychotic medicine, Sally sleeps better and is calmer, less irritable. She smiles and sits quietly in the chair across from me. "I liked our Scout campout — it was fun!" Sally shares with me. She is beginning to make friends finally.

At age eight: Sally tells me about a friend she enjoys and also shares sad feelings: "I'm sad my dog died. I want to go to heaven and bring my dog back."

At age nine: Sally is smiling as she tells me, "I had fun at the zoo with my Dad! I'm looking forward to fourth grade starting soon!" Her connection to her family and her comfort with school have greatly improved.

In summary, Sally now age nine, demonstrates less sadness and irritability and much more cheerfulness than when I first met her when she was six. It has been a pleasure to help her feel better and to help her find that life can be enjoyable. I can now say the word "tornado" to Sally without her cringing. She can say it too, and laugh at herself for the great fears that word used to bring down upon her. And we continue our work together as she approaches her preteen and teen years.

An Angry Teen Turns Pleasant

Frank is a teen with Bipolar Disorder. In the last few years, this diagnosis has become controversial within the psychiatric community. It is a diagnosis that recently is applied more frequently to teens and children than it was in the past. We know that among adults, one to two percent will suffer from this disorder, most being diagnosed in their young adult years. Dr. March, Chief of Child and Adolescent Psychiatry at Duke University, told the "New York Times" in an interview September of 2007: "We don't know how accurately we can diagnose Bipolar in children and teens and whether those diagnosed Bipolar at ages five, six and seven will be adults with Bipolar." There is confusion and discord in this area of psychiatry. With this in mind, let me tell you Frank's story.

Frank, a fifteen-year-old boy, and his Dad, Mr. Melody, sit before me for our first meeting. Frank, a tall, lean teenager, talks loudly and rapidly from the moment he enters my office until he and his father leave an hour later. He fidgets in his chair and does not appear to notice me. His words are what psychiatrists call tangential, meaning he jumps from one topic to another, then to another, unrelated one. His talk is intrusive, unrestrained. Most kids new to me will hold back in shyness until they are comfortable with me. Not Frank. He jokes with his Dad as I try to ask his father about Frank's current problems and his background.

"Frank, I need you to wait to talk until I finish asking your father some questions about your background," I insert between Frank's ramblings. Frank, dressed in jeans, a t-shirt with a bizarre-looking video game character, his hair below his ears, but neatly combed, is wound up tight as a spring. Frank appears to be hypomanic, an engine out of control. Frank's counselor at our clinic had told me that in the family sessions, Frank had become explosive and was asked to leave the counselor's office to calm himself down. In this interview with me, Frank calms down at my request, allowing me to learn about his background from his father.

Frank's father continues: "He was diagnosed with ADHD (Attention Deficit Hyperactivity Disorder) in the second grade by the family doctor, and he has been on medicine for that all these years. He was on the honor roll until this year in eighth grade, when his grades dropped to Cs and Ds. At home, he refuses to follow our rules, and this year for the first time his behavior with kids in our neighborhood got him in trouble. He hit a kid who was teasing him and the kid's parents were very upset with Frank, and so were we. We took him to a counselor after that crisis, but he refused to talk, so we stopped taking him after two months. He won't go to bed until one in the morning, but he doesn't seem tired during the day."

Frank's father is a nice-looking man dressed in a business suit. The frustration in his voice and the tenseness of his body language convey that dealing with Frank is difficult. "After his girlfriend broke off with him, Frank threatened to kill himself. That's why we brought him here for counseling and to see you for some medication," Mr. Melody adds.

"Do any of Frank's relatives have Attention Deficit Hyperactivity Disorder or Bipolar Disorder?" I ask.

"Yes, as a matter of fact, my sister was told she has both Bipolar Disorder and Attention Deficit Disorder. Frank's behaviors remind me of my sister," Mr. Melody replies.

"We know that Bipolar Disorder has a genetic component. In addition to the genetic part, stress also plays an important role in triggering a manic or depressive episode," I explain to Frank and Mr. Melody.

Further questions about Frank's history reveal that his mother's pregnancy with him was normal; she did not smoke or use alcohol during the pregnancy. So there was no known damage to his brain during the pregnancy or in the birth process. Frank has no history of being physically or sexually abused. He has problems making friends and is often teased by kids at school.

"Frank, I'd like to ask you some questions now. These questions are difficult ones and may make you uncomfortable, but they are ones I ask all the teens I work with. Take your time in answering them. Do you ever have thoughts of wanting to kill yourself?"

"Once, when my girlfriend dumped me a couple of months ago, I did," Frank answers with no hesitation.

"Have you had thoughts of wanting to kill others?" I ask.

"I'd like to beat up some of the kids who call me 'hyper guy,' but I've never thought of using something to kill them with," Frank replies.

This question, about having thoughts and plans of killing others, I always ask, in light of the Columbine High School shootings as well as other shootings in grade schools, high schools, and colleges. Studies of the Columbine killers suggested they were kids who were teased repeatedly, their resulting rage reaching murderous proportions. Children are amazingly honest about murderous feelings if direct questions are asked of them. Fortunately, Frank's anger about being teased has not reached a dangerous level; he has violent thoughts of hitting those who tease him, but not of killing them.

"Frank, please tell me a dream you have had at night when you are sleeping," I request.

"In one dream, I am attacked by monsters. In another one, I am falling down the stairs in our house. Both are scary," Frank explains.

"Dreams of being chased represent that you are worried about something, and your dream of falling suggests sadness. Are you aware of being sad or worried?" I ask Frank.

"I was depressed after my two grandmas died and after my girlfriend dumped me. I worry about not having many friends and about being teased," Frank shares.

"Tell me what you'd wish for to make your life better, Frank."

"I'd wish to be a famous singer and the best snowboarder in the world! And to have a hot girlfriend."

"So you want to be tops in music and sports as well as with girls," I summarize.

"I appreciate you being very open with your feelings and thoughts, Frank. Thank you." As I turn back to Frank's father I say, "Let's review how I understand Frank's problems. Frank appears to have both ADHD and Bipolar problems. He is on medication for the ADHD and this has helped him focus on his schoolwork and improve his grades. Continuing with his individual and family counseling is important, too. In addition, I suggest a medication for the mania he has now. We use several kinds of medicines to prevent mood swings: lithium carbonate, anticonvulsant and antipsychotic drugs. Any one or several in combination can bring the manic mood to a normal level of energy. Side effects of some of these medications are weight gain and in increase risk for development of diabetes and heart disease."

Frank's father decides to try Frank on a small dose of an antipsychotic medication. Frank is angry about having to take another medication in addition to his ADHD medicine. I try to empathize with him as well as to explain how the medicine may help him reduce conflict with family and friends. We agree to meet again in four weeks.

· · · · · · · · · ● · · · · · · · · · ·

Four weeks later, I am meeting Frank's mother for the first time, along with Frank. She is an attractive woman, dressed in slacks and a crisp blouse. She and Frank are energetically arguing as they enter my office, and this continues throughout the twenty-minute session. This conflict I take as a sign that Frank's mania has not diminished much. Frank's mother reports that his irritability is a little better, but only slightly so. "The improvement is that he's only had one big outburst in the last four weeks. He's sleeping better, too. I think the medicine is beginning to work," his mother reports.

"I feel tired," Frank chimes in, displeased with the sedating side effect of his new medicine.

"The tiredness may lessen with time, Frank. Let's keep an eye on it. Bipolar people are used to a very high energy level and often do not like feeling a lower energy level. I noticed on the ADHD questionnaire I had you give to your teachers to complete, that some noticed you looking sad."

"I am sad when kids talk bad about me," Frank states.

"Frank, be sure to talk with your counselor about this very important topic of being teased and sad. He can help you develop skills for making friends and dealing with the teasing. Your parents and you should also talk to the school staff about the teasing and what anti-bullying policies they have. Most school's since the Columbine shootings have adopted ways to handle bullying between students and are taking this problem more seriously."

· · · · · · · ● · · · · · · · · ·

As I continue to see Frank and his parents over the following year, his mania and irritability calm dramatically. He no longer argues constantly with his parents. His parents have learned to not engage in conflict with him on minor issues. Frank is not fighting with other kids and his grades are good. However, he has gained weight from the antipsychotic and is unhappy about this. Blood work shows his cholesterol and sugar levels are normal. We decide to switch to an antipsychotic that is less likely to cause weight gain. Frank is pleased as he sheds twenty pounds.

He gets a job and is able to be responsible and not have conflict with his boss and fellow workers. He learns to play drums and feels success in his music. He makes some good choices to avoid using illegal drugs his friends are using and to not follow his friends who plan to vandalize a neighbor's home. As his self-esteem improves, he is less vulnerable to teasing.

Frank is on a better path than he was when I first met him. Bipolar Disorder is a life-long illness, marked by cycles of depression and mania. Frank may require mental health services throughout his life. Hopefully his experience with me and his counselor will allow him to reach out for help as he needs it in his adult years.

CHAPTER SEVEN

Childhood Anxiety Disorder

THIS CHAPTER WILL introduce you to several forms anxiety can take in childhood and the children with whom I worked.

Symptoms of Panic Disorder

- Sudden onset of intense fear (panic attacks see Symptoms of Panic Attack later in this chapter) with no obvious cause, usually lasting five to ten minutes.
- Sudden onset during the panic attack of physical symptoms such as pounding heart, sweating, shaking, a feeling of smothering and choking, chest pain, nausea and stomach pain, dizziness, chills, hot flashes, hands numb and tingling from breathing too rapidly (hyperventilation); feeling one is dying or going crazy.
- Anticipatory anxiety often occurs, which is a fear that the panic attacks will return.

Agoraphobia sometimes but not always accompanies Panic Disorder. Agoraphobia is a fear of being unable to escape a situation, usually when in a public place as follows:

- Feeling of being trapped, usually occurring outside the home: for example, panic when in line at the grocery, at a movie, on a bridge, in a car.

- Avoids going to the feared places outside the home.
- Stays home most of the time.

Adapted from DSM-5

The Boy With Panic Disorder

"You've seen almost the whole family now," Mrs. Beam is telling me with a resigned smile, "me, my daughter, Pam, my nephew, and now John, my youngest, for our panic problems. I already told you my mother and my grandmother both have panic attacks." Mrs. Beam is a tall, gangly woman with barely combed hair and rumpled but clean clothes. She has always looked the same over the three years I have worked with her and various members of her family. Is it the same shirt and slacks, or just similar? I know her to be a committed mother who struggles to raise her family, but who never complains about the unfairness of this pernicious disease that runs through at least three generations of her family. Mrs. Beam has been raising her four children alone since her husband abandoned the family several years ago. She is unable to work because leaving the home sets off her panic attacks. Finances are tight, but her children are well-fed and adequately clothed.

I enjoy working with a family who has trust in me from three years of working together and one with whom I feel a comfortable rapport. I don't need to ask her questions, because she knows the interview process better than she might like.

"I know this may sound like I'm making something out of nothing, but I think John is developing panic attacks just like me and his sister. He never had any problems until this year in fifth grade. He has been a good student and well-behaved at school with lots of friends. The school thinks I am making excuses for him."

I think to myself, I know that anxiety disorders run in families, but to this degree?

"John enjoys his friends at school, so I want to work with the school to keep him there. When it is time to leave for school, John is eager to go. But as we drive closer to school, he hyperventilates, sweats and shakes, and has chest pains. I walk him into school, but he often can't stay or if he stays the nurse is calling me an hour later to pick him up. John has always been a worrier, but it got much worse when his brother was hospitalized and diagnosed with pneumonia six months ago. He watches his brother like a hawk and worries that the dog will get run over and that a burglar will break in. Of course, his dad leaving when he was eight upset all of us, but he doesn't talk much about missing his dad. He has missed twelve days of school this year and the school is threatening to send the truant officer after me."

"Did John have trouble leaving you when he started kindergarten?" I ask. "No, he loves school and never had trouble going until a couple of months ago."

John's problem does not appear to be separation anxiety, a situation in which kids avoid going to school out of fear that one or both parents will die in an accident or will become ill and die. That usually starts in kindergarten. John has told me today that he isn't fearful his mother will die or leave him as his father did.

"Any family stress in the past three months?" I always ask about significant changes in a family, such as deaths, divorce, and illness, when the child's behavior has suddenly changed.

"No, nothing other than his brother's pneumonia six months ago. That really upset all of us."

John's history tells me he has not experienced physical or sexual abuse; the pregnancy with him was normal and his development has been normal.

I turn to John with my usual questions, which he answers timidly but thoughtfully. "What are your three wishes, John, to make your life better?"

"A new car for mom and money to pay the bills and buy me some video games. And for our family to do fun things together more."

John is a kid sensitive to his mother's financial struggles, but he has room in his wishes for himself. That's good.

"Tell me a dream you have had during the night." I know after years of asking this question not to ask "Have you had a dream?"

Kids always say "No" unless I say: "Tell me a dream you've had while you are sleeping." A nightmare of monsters or werewolves tells me a child is having anxiety. A nightmare of falling indicates depression. A funny dream means life is good for now. Dreams are a barometer of a child's inner state of mind. Often as I work along with a child, I will see the nightmares disappear as the child loses his anxiety or sadness, and be replaced by happy or funny dreams. My interest in dreams is a remnant of influence by Sigmund Freud, the creator of psychiatry and one of my heroes.

"They are hard to remember....but they are bad ones. I jump off of something in one, but that's all I know."

"Jumping or falling in a dream often means the person is sad or depressed. Dreams are important John, so as you remember them, share them with your mom and your counselor. They tell you about your deeper, hidden feelings." The power of my suggestion may help John begin to remember his dreams in greater detail.

Turning to his mother, I say, "Well, you are an old hand at this. You know the medicines we use – an antidepressant medication for the anxiety and for the panic attacks. It takes two to four weeks to work. There is a warning on using antidepressants in children because some children have been noted to develop suicidal ideas while on them. John does not have thoughts of suicide, but I will ask him about them each time I see him and you should be alert for them, too. Since he is only sleeping six hours, let's try a mild medicine to boost this to the nine hours most kids need."

Wow, a family with three known generations of panic disorder and within John's generation at least three family members so far – John, his older sister, and a cousin.

• • • • • • • • ● • • • • • • • •

As I work over the school year with John, progress in his attendance in fifth grade is slow – slower than I expect. I'm beginning to think I have set my expectations too high and need to lower them to small steps instead of big leaps. I increase his antidepressant medicine and add a small amount of an anti-anxiety medicine to calm him half an hour before he leaves for school. The school has been uncooperative with John's mother because they feel John and his mother are inventing an excuse to skip school. So I suggest she contact a free service that will provide an advocate who will go with her to the school to request special accommodations for John.

The advocate's involvement leads to the school's decision to have John attend class in the mornings only. This seems to me to be a reasonable expectation for John, given the stage of his illness. John has been able to meet the school's goal for several weeks in a row. He has taken a small but significant step forward. By the end of the year, he succeeds in passing fifth grade.

Next year will be even more challenging, because John will enter junior high school, where he must change classes and teachers throughout the day. This transition into junior high school causes most kids anxiety; John will have a double dose of "nerves." Summer will be a time for him to practice leaving the house with his mother, going to the grocery and to other places that create anxiety for him. He will start with the situation least scary for him and add increasingly difficult situations. If he avoids these situations completely, his anxiety will skyrocket, since the imagined is always worse than the reality. He will likely need accommodations at school again next fall. The accommodation plan should include gradually lengthening his time at school to a full day.

Once in sixth grade, John becomes paralyzed by his anxiety. At one appointment he is near tears and he says he is very upset to not be able to attend all of his classes, especially the one on how to use the microscope.

"My one teacher said she'd twist my head around if I didn't come to school each day." John is frustrated and so am I.

His mother decides at this point to home school him as she had done John's older sister, Pam, because of her Panic Disorder. She completed high school through an on-line program sponsored by a university. She then attended a community college, followed by going away from home to a four year college where she was able to manage her anxiety. Since John is also bright, he was able to complete middle school through homeschooling. Once he reaches high school, John asks to return to public school since he is missing his friends. John and I part ways because I move away. However, I have confidence he will finish high school one way or another and go on to college as his older sister was able to do.

Panic Attack Symptoms

Intense fear in which four or more of the following symptoms develop suddenly and reach a peak within ten minutes:

- Palpitations, pounding heart or fast heart rate
- Sweating
- Trembling or shaking
- Feeling short of breath or a smothering feeling
- Feeling of choking
- Chest pain
- Nausea or abdominal discomfort
- Feeling dizzy or faint
- Derealization (feeling of unreality) or depersonalization (feeling detached from oneself)
- Fear of losing control or going crazy
- Fear of dying
- Numbness or tingling sensations
- Chills or hot flushes

Adapted from American Psychiatric Association's DSM-5

The Teen With Panic Attacks and Derealization

Rick asked his mother to take him to talk to a psychiatrist, so he has come willingly today with his mother to see me. He is a fifteen-year-old with dark hair that covers his eyes, like that of an English sheepdog. He stands at least six feet tall and is neatly dressed in khaki pants and a blue- collared shirt. While he is polite and pleasant as we talk, I notice he does not smile even once during the interview. Not being able to see Rick's eyes makes it hard for me to read his feelings, but the absent smile tells me of his sadness.

Rick has no trouble answering when I ask him to explain his concern to me: "It was New Year's Eve and I was staying overnight at a friend's house. I had not been to his house before and suddenly I couldn't catch my breath, my heart started pounding and my hands got sweaty. I thought I was dying! I had to call Mom to come and pick me up. That next week in school I had the same thing happen. It took me half an hour to calm myself down."

"You have just described a panic attack, Rick," I explain.

"But even worse than these two attacks is the feeling I have had several times over the last year where I feel that nothing around me is real," Rick says.

"You are describing what we psychiatrists call derealization – where things do not seem real to you. This feeling seems to happen mainly to teenagers and can be very upsetting. Fortunately it is not a sign of serious mental illness, but it is a sign of being under lots of stress," I explain.

Rick's mother, a proper looking woman who sits back and lets Rick tell his own story, answers my question about relatives who have anxiety problems. "Yes, there is anxiety on both sides of Rick's family. Rick's Dad has anxiety, his aunt on his Dad's side, and his uncle on my side."

"We know that anxiety problems run in families," I explain. "There are two types of medicines we use: antidepressant medicines help with the panic attacks. Anti-anxiety medicines help the panic, but we only recommend them for a few weeks since they are addictive. Weekly counseling is important in combination with the medications. Learning to control the panic can often be accomplished through use of relaxation techniques."

When I ask Rick what he wishes most for, he answers: "To feel normal and for the world to be at peace."

"I'll see you and your mother in four weeks to see if the antidepressant medicine I would like to start you on is helping your anxiety and to see how your counseling is going," I summarize.

"Goodbye, Doctor, and thanks for listening to me," Rick says as he leaves the office.

I admit I find adolescents difficult to work with because of the intense inner turmoil and acting out they go through to arrive at the other side called adulthood. But it is kids like Rick, with their idealism and wish for the world to be at peace, that give me hope for the younger generation and for the world.

· · · · · · ●●● ● ●●● · · · · · ·

Over the following months, Rick makes good progress on calming his anxiety and panic attacks. His derealization also ceases once he learns to be aware of and talk through his worries and stress with family and friends.

Obsessive Compulsive Disorder Symptoms

OBSESSIONS are repetitive thoughts and fears that will not go away and that make little sense to the person experiencing them. The obsessions can be about:

- fears of being contaminated by germs
- fears of losing control of angry or sexual feelings
- insistent thoughts that possessions must be arranged symmetrically
- fearing you may cause harm to another
- over-concern that one is sinning
- superstitions about lucky or unlucky numbers or colors

COMPULSIONS are repetitive behaviors that make no sense to the person experiencing them, but that are done to prevent a dreaded event from happening. Common compulsions are:

- excessive hand-washing or showering, many times in a day
- cleaning one's house to an extreme
- checking and re-checking numerous times that one did something correctly,
- such as locking doors or turning off the stove
- Re-reading

- Re-writing
- going in and out of doors; getting in and out of chairs or bed
- tapping, touching repeatedly
- repeating acts in sets of threes or some other number, for safety
- collecting/hoarding items
- putting items in order until it feels right
- needing constant reassurance

This list is adapted from the International OCD Foundation, Inc. found at www.ocfoundation.org.

A Teenager with Obsessive Compulsive Disorder

What are the behaviors that define Obsessive Compulsive Disorder (OCD)? When I lock my front door as I leave for work in the morning, I may re-check it once, to be sure I really locked it. Re-checking once is enough to assure me that the door is locked. An OCD person might have to check numerous times after locking his door to be reassured that he locked it, and might still feel uneasy, as if something were left undone, even after multiple checks and re-checks.

Many of us have perfectionist and compulsive traits. For example, I dislike clutter, and if my husband stacks his papers on the dining room table, I feel unsettled until the papers are put away. Recently, a friend confessed to me that she counts the wheels on semi trucks as she passes them on the highway. She worried that this meant she had OCD. However, a diagnosis of OCD requires that the obsessive thoughts and routines such as counting, must take up an hour or more of one's day, must cause distress, and must interfere with one's work and social life. My friend breathed a sigh of relief when I explained this to her. I suggested that she might simply be nervous when driving near semis, and she could tell herself: "I'm afraid this semi I am passing will crash into me." By acknowledging the fear, the compulsion to count the semi's wheels might evaporate.

The person with OCD takes his obsession with cleaning to an extreme, making it a repetitive, time-consuming ritual, done even when the house is tidy and clean. You've seen a mother cat licking her kittens. She knows when the licking is enough and her brain tells her to stop licking. The brain of the person with OCD has lost its ability to tell the person "it's time to stop; it's enough." OCD is an engulfing illness that causes the individual much suffering.

If you watch the television show "Monk," you will see an accurate depiction of an adult (the detective Monk) with Obsessive Compulsive Disorder. Monk's attention to minute details makes him a good detective, but his compulsive rituals often interfere with his work. If it weren't for his secretary pulling his focus away from his rituals, he would not solve many mysteries. Monk is obsessed with the thought that germs cover all surfaces he touches, and he fears he will become infected with these germs. His compulsive behaviors include scrubbing his hands numerous times after someone has shaken his hand. About two out of 100 adults have OCD; half of them had OCD symptoms beginning in childhood.

What do we know about OCD in children and teenagers? One out of every 200 American youth have OCD. Here are some of the rituals seen in children and teens: keeping possessions symmetrical and balanced; checking and rechecking locks on their homes to keep out imagined intruders; thinking repeatedly of certain numbers to keep danger away; climbing in and out of bed a certain number of times before being able to fall asleep for the night; stepping only on odd-numbered steps in order to feel safe. Remember the saying we had as children: "Step on a crack and break your mother's back?" We stepped over cracks in the sidewalk supposedly in order to avoid hurting our mothers. The person with OCD uses similar obsessive thoughts and compulsive behaviors to avoid bringing harm to herself or another.

Let me introduce you to Kathy, a teenager with OCD. Kathy is a fifteen-year-old, stylish teen with long, dark, wavy hair, dressed in black slacks and a red, dressy blouse. Her make up is carefully applied and her voluminous hair is subdued by a red headband. Kathy looks tense as she and her mother enter my office for their first appointment. The look on her face is not of sadness, but there is an absence of emotional expression that alerts me to distress in a patient.

"Kathy, can you tell me about your problems?" I ask her.

"Well, I have to line up my make-up, my clothes, and my books just so. I check in a mirror constantly to see if my hair is in place and my make up on perfectly. Mom and I think I have OCD."

"Kathy, these do sound like compulsive behaviors - the need for symmetry and the sense of doubting that you have done something perfectly, so that you have to check again and again. We think the psychological purpose of these repetitive behaviors is to make you feel safe from some kind of harm you fear will come to you. Kids are often embarrassed about the rituals and try to hide them from friends and family, but, like your mother, parents often notice these repeated behaviors in their children. We know that OCD runs in families, so I want to ask your mother if any relatives on her side or your father's side have OCD."

"Yes," Mrs. Smith replies. "Kathy's great-grandfather and her great- uncle both have OCD. My mother and I are both perfectionists, but we don't have OCD."

I think to myself that Kathy has a large genetic load for OCD. We know that genetics play a major role in OCD, although the specific gene has not been identified. How do we know it is inherited? By looking at identical twins. If one identical twin has OCD, the other twin has a 60% chance of having OCD as well.

Mrs. Smith continues: "I also think Kathy is depressed; she talks of suicide when she gets angry with her sister for messing up the bedroom they share." Kathy's mother is a concerned parent whose blond hair is pulled back into a ponytail. Her outfit and make up are less perfect than her daughter's. She's more relaxed. "Kathy's been keeping more to herself the last five months. I worry because my father had depressions that required him to be hospitalized several times over the years."

"Kathy, tell me about your thoughts of suicide. How often do these thoughts enter your mind, and do you have a plan of how to kill yourself?"

"Thoughts of being dead come into my mind every day. Death would be peaceful, an escape. I don't have a plan to kill myself and I've never tried to. I just get so frustrated with my sister. She keeps our bedroom a mess and it upsets me because I like things neat."

"Yes, Kathy, I can see how your sister's messiness is upsetting your strong need for symmetry and tidiness. Mrs. Smith, can we ask your daughter to help decrease Kathy's distress by being more tidy until Kathy gets better?"

As we review other parts of Kathy's life, I learn she is an honor roll student with plans to study engineering in college. She has good social skills and many friends. She has never been physically or sexually abused and has not experimented with nicotine, marijuana, or alcohol. There are many positive factors in Kathy's life I am pleased to learn. The absence of poor grades, drug addition, sexual or physical abuse, and social skills problems will make the healing process from OCD less complicated.

"Let's talk about the treatment we use for OCD. One part is medication, the other part is counseling. Regarding medications, the antidepressants increase serotonin levels in the brain that are thought to be low in OCD. Antipsychotic medications may also help. The type of counseling specific to OCD is called exposure therapy, in which the patient is exposed to small amounts of what he or she fears and learns to tolerate it without acting out the safeguarding ritual. Both types of treatment are important and complement each other.

"For you, Kathy, I suggest in addition to weekly exposure therapy, an antidepressant medication which will help the depression and the OCD symptoms. Antidepressants take two to four weeks to help the depression and may take several months and higher doses to help the obsessive thinking and the rituals, so be patient." We discuss the possible side effects and Kathy and her mother agree to try an antidepressant.

· · · · · · ● ● · ● ● ● · · · · · · ·

When I see Kathy and her mother a month later, Kathy's suicidal ideas are gone and her depression has improved. Not surprisingly, her OCD symptoms have not decreased. Kathy shares a new symptom with me: "I'm having these times where I space out and don't feel things around me are real. I've had that for four months and it happens about once a month. It really upsets me."

"Kathy, that sounds like what we call 'derealization.' It means—just as you describe it—that you feel things around you are not real. It is common in teens when they are under stress. It does not mean you are going crazy, just that you are feeling great stress. There is no medication for this.

"Now that your depression is better, are you interested in increasing the dose of the antidepressant to see if it can help your OCD? The idea is to increase the dose gradually until we find the amount needed to decrease your obsessions and rituals."

Kathy and her mother agree to this plan.

• • • • • • • • ● • • • • • • • • • •

It is a month later and Kathy reports that she has fewer obsessive thoughts about neatness and symmetry, but still has to check in mirrors often to see that her makeup is on perfectly. The slight increase in the antidepressant dose has started to help her OCD, but only slightly. Kathy and her mother agree to increase the antidepressant medication another notch, hoping it will lower the obsessions and compulsions even further. We review again the several relatives with OCD and I emphasize to Kathy that this illness is genetic and not something she brought upon herself. She looks more relaxed today, and she smiles.

• • • • • • • • ● • • • • • • • • • •

At our next follow-up appointment, Kathy is having both fewer obsessions and fewer compulsions. She is feeling a wonderful sense of freedom from the burden they have been to her. Her mother is pleased to see her daughter smiling and feeling less weighed down with her rituals, and happy to see Kathy and her sister getting along better. We agree to meet in four months to check on Kathy's progress. Kathy's counseling will continue with work on her self-esteem and desensitization for her fears.

Social Anxiety Disorder Symptoms

- anxiety that comes on in social situations, often accompanied by shame and embarrassment and trouble making eye contact
- fear of saying something stupid or humiliating
- fear of talking with a teacher or a peer
- fear of talking on the phone
- fear of answering a question aloud in class
- fear of meeting new people
- fear of eating in public, using public bathrooms
- fear of shopping or driving
- social situations are avoided to prevent the anxiety
- job and school attendance may be decreased because of fears
- physical expression of fear such as sweating, rapid heartbeat, upset stomach, trembling, dry mouth, blushing, breathing fast

Adapted from DSM-5

The Painfully Shy Teenager

Fred is a hulk of a young man, standing over six feet tall. A striking feature is his four-inch-long, very thick bangs, which hang over his eyes like a lead shield. His head is lowered, hiding his face as well. This puts me at a disadvantage, since I depend so much on a patient's facial expression and his eyes – are they sad, blank, or twinkling? His flatly spoken words hide his feelings as well. But today Fred is indirectly telling me about his shyness and maybe his sadness by hiding his face and by slumping his upper body over my desk.

Fred's mother, Mrs. Stratta, a concerned and caring woman in her fifties, is explaining Fred's problem as she sees it: "He hasn't talked to anyone his age all summer. He has a few friends at school, but why doesn't he call one of them or get together with one? His family doctor started him on an antidepressant medicine a couple of months ago and since then he seems more cheerful around the house. He talks to us more than he did, but still he doesn't call his friends."

Fred pipes up, "I don't like people. They bore me. I'm not depressed. I'm happy being a loner!" Fred is dressed today in jeans and a plain t-shirt, and on the outside he looks like any teenager, except for the hiding of his face. He raises his head and shakes his hair off to the side long enough to briefly make eye contact with me in an effort to convey his opinion.

"I had friends in grade school, but in junior high I got harassed and pushed around and laughed at. Now I just stay away from everyone so they'll ignore me and they do."

Withdrawal from peers can be part of depression, or it can be caused by anxiety the teenager feels around peers. Teens are often somewhat anxious around peers, but when the anxiety is severe, this may be a social anxiety disorder.

"Does anyone in the family have shyness now or as a child or teen?"

"Well," Fred's mother replies, "I was very shy in high school and never had friends. That's what upsets me about Fred. I don't want him to go through the loneliness I felt those four years."

"Shyness often runs in families. Sometimes parents who were shy as children or teens outgrow this as they become adults. Mrs. Stratta, you remember your own shyness and while this similarity makes you worried, it also helps you empathize with your son. Is your husband shy?" I ask.

"Yes, he hardly talks to anyone other than to me. He was shy as a child too, but never outgrew it as I have. I hope Fred can overcome his shyness," Mrs. Stratta explains.

"The treatment for Fred's shyness has two parts: one is counseling, to work on becoming comfortable with others; the other is taking an antidepressant medication to help with his anxiety. Usually high doses are needed to find relief from Social Anxiety Disorder. With anxiety occurring on both sides of Fred's family, the chances for improvement are limited. Sometimes anti-anxiety medicines can be used to bring relief as a patient ventures out among people," I explain.

Fred and his mother agree to both counseling and to an antidepressant. I will see him in a month to assess his progress.

· · · · · · ● · · · · · · · · · ·

It is 6 months later and I am seeing Fred and his mother for the fifth time. Fred has been attending his weekly counseling sessions. He seems relaxed today with me and when we review his anxiety around his peers, he is able to see some improvement. Fred is committed to working further on his anxiety and shyness and his prognosis is good.

Symptoms of Selective Mutism

- A child with Selective Mutism speaks normally within the family, but does not speak aloud in school or other public places.
- Selective Mutism is often first noticed by the family and school when the child enters preschool or kindergarten.
- The child with Selective Mutism is often shy and may have parents who were shy as children.
- A child who experiences an emotional trauma may stop speaking for a few weeks, but does not have Selective Mutism unless the mutism continues for months.
- The child with Selective Mutism is of normal intelligence.
- Half of children with Selective Mutism have an articulation or other language problem.
- Selective Mutism is thought to be caused by anxiety.
- Treatment includes use of antidepressant medications to increase serotonin in the brain, a rewards program to reinforce whispering and speaking aloud, speech therapy, and counseling to decrease shyness and anxiety about speaking outside the home.
- Pressuring the child to speak does not work.
- As the child slowly improves, she will whisper to teachers and friends, then gradually use a normal speaking voice.

- When these children become adults, they may be nervous around people and may speak infrequently in social settings.

Adapted from DSM-5

How Anxiety Keeps Children From Talking

Selective Mutism is a diagnosis applied when a child does not speak in settings outside the home such as school, church, or the grocery, yet is able to speak normally in the home. First named as a psychiatric disorder in 1877, it develops before the age of five, but is usually not identified until the child enters school, where a teacher notices that the child refuses to talk to her or to other students.

I should put this rare illness in perspective—it affects less than one out of one hundred American children. The cause is thought to be a child's intense anxiety in social settings outside the familiarity of home. I remember a classmate of mine, Judy, who was so very shy that she never spoke to anyone in the classroom, in the cafeteria, or on the bus, and would only occasionally glance at other kids. I especially remember Judy's experience when, in the eighth grade, we had to memorize the Gettysburg Address for government class. As each of us came to the front of the classroom to recite what we had memorized, many of us were shaking inside. When it was Judy's turn, she walked reluctantly to the front of the room, her head hanging down and her whole body quivering. We all seemed to be holding our collective breath as we wondered if she could do this. Standing in front of the class Judy spoke the first line: "Four score and seven years ago…" Then, hiding her face in both hands, she burst into tears and ran back to her desk. The teacher, mercifully, moved on to the next student. The enormity of Judy's fear stuck vividly in my mind, and I believe, looking back, that she had Selective Mutism. With current psychiatric knowledge she could be helped with her silent suffering if her parents were willing to seek professional help. We, her fellow students, certainly noticed that she was miserable. I have developed a theory from years of working with children, that playmates often are aware of another child's insecurities and emotional suffering. The proof of my theory is supported by these observations: classroom bullies know which kids have low self-esteem and select them as their victims; and kids know who the class clown is, who is sad or shy, and who is mean. We adults rarely think to ask kids for this valuable information.

During my career as a child psychiatrist, I have worked with five children with Selective Mutism, and while that is a small number, the illness is so dramatic that these children have remained ingrained in my mind. My first patient with Selective Mutism was a boy named Billy. When his mother brought him to see me, it was early in my career and I was puzzled by this boy who spoke at home but not at school. To figure out his diagnosis, I referred to the Diagnostic and Statistical Manual (DSM) written by the American Psychiatric Association. Billy was a cute, sandy-haired boy of five. His mother said he talked at home, but he simply refused to speak to his kindergarten teacher or his classmates. Prozac had just come on the market for the treatment of depression and I read in one of my psychiatric journals that Prozac had helped a child with Selective Mutism. Back then, psychiatrists had no idea how Prozac could help a child be less shy and anxious and thus begin to talk. But since there weren't any other options, I thought it was worth trying Billy on Prozac, and his mother agreed. Some 20 years later, we learned that Prozac decreases anxiety, which may be the mechanism by which it helps children with Selective Mutism. Gradually, Billy began to speak aloud at school and at church, and within a year he was cured of Selective Mutism. His mother was determined to get him talking, so she did not hesitate to use Prozac along with some ideas I gave her to introduce her son gradually to more and more social situations. Thanks to the DSM book, my reading about Prozac, and Billy's mother's willingness to try a new medicine and work on his social skills, he made amazing progress.

I have included a discussion of Selective Mutism in this book for those families who are perplexed by a child who is talkative at home, yet refuses to speak at school or in other public places. Since teachers are often the first to notice that a child is not speaking to anyone in the school setting, this chapter is also for school staff who find this disorder particularly perplexing, often mistakenly seeing the child as just being stubborn and therefore pressuring the child to speak.

How does Selective Mutism compare to other emotional disorders in childhood where speaking is a problem? Selective Mutism and Autism share the lack of speaking, yet are very different disorders. The child with Selective Mutism has good emotional attachment and eye contact with family members, and speaks readily to them when at home, but is filled with anxiety with people outside his family. The Autistic child, in contrast, is detached emotionally from people both at home and at school. The child with Selective Mutism uses gestures with friends on the playground to show his interest in playing with them, while the autistic child prefers to be alone.

Tim is a recent patient of mine who has Selective Mutism. When I first met Tim, he was a nine-year-old, handsome boy with short brown hair. At his first appointment with me, I noticed that his brown eyes were full of fear, and he avoided even a glance of curiosity in my direction as he entered my office. He came in close behind his mother, sat in a chair that he pulled next to her chair, and turned his head and body towards her, not changing his position for the full hour. His shyness was extreme.

Mrs. Jay told me of her concerns about Tim. "Tim got kicked out of school because of his fighting. When kids tease him about not talking at school, Tim hits them. Tim won't speak to his friends or to his teachers and he hasn't since he entered kindergarten. Now he is in the fourth grade. He won't speak to anyone at stores or church or any place except at home. At home he talks a lot, although with some articulation problems." Mrs. Jay is a middle-aged woman with short brown hair. Her blouse and slacks are practical. She is, I will learn over the coming five years, a concerned and devoted mother who is persistent about her son improving. Every doctor dreams of such highly motivated parents with whom to work. She and Tim have been a delight to work with over these five years. Although progress has been painfully slow, Tim and his mother have persisted, trusting in the process of the treatment program we set up for Tim at our clinic. Those of us helping Tim have taken pleasure in watching him gradually improve.

At the beginning of the first interview that I have with a new patient and his parents, I ask the parents to voice their concerns about their child. This step is important not only as a time for me to collect information about the key problems, but also as a time to make the child more fully aware of his problem behaviors. His parents are stating the facts of the child's behaviors to me, sometimes matter-of-factly, and sometimes with great frustration. These are the problems that the child must begin to view as unacceptable behaviors, ones to explore and examine. Tim began squirming in his chair when his mother described to me his fighting at school and his mutism. Thus began Tim's journey to look at himself with a critical eye in a supportive atmosphere.

In reviewing Tim's family history with his mother, I learned that Tim's father and mother had each been intensely shy as children. As Tim's parents grew into adulthood each became more at ease with people outside their families. Today, Tim's mother speaks comfortably with me; his father, however, remains painfully uncomfortable in social settings.

Studies show that parents of children with Selective Mutism were often shy as children and may continue to be uncomfortable in social situations as adults, but less so than they were in childhood. Do family members pass this trait down to the younger generation? Genetic studies have not examined Selective Mutism, but studies do show that some forms of anxiety are inherited.

Tim's mother continued. "It's the fighting that got him removed from school and referred to your clinic's school program."

Before Tim came to us, he was in Special Education at his public school because of his dyslexia. Once he began to be involved in fights at school, the school decreased his school time to two hours each day. When Tim continued fighting and was on the verge of expulsion, his principal referred him to our clinic's education program. Our clinic provides a school setting for children with disruptive behaviors, ones who threaten the safety of their classmates and teachers, and those on the verge of being expelled. Our clinic's teachers provide a curriculum appropriate to each child, allowing the child to continue earning school credits. Once the child has improved his behavior, he returns to public school.

I turned to Tim and his mother at the end of our first interview to begin to summarize my understanding of Tim's problem. "Tim appears to have Selective Mutism. Selective Mustism is thought to be a problem of anxiety and shyness. We treat this disorder with medications, speech therapy, and counseling. I suggest we try Tim on an antidepressant medicine that may help him feel less nervous about speaking aloud. As he begins to talk to people beyond your home, I believe his fighting will lessen. He will learn from his counseling sessions how to express his anger through words instead of through his actions. And his speech therapy will help him pronounce words more clearly."

"Will Tim become addicted to this medicine? I worry that it will give him a high feeling." Mrs. Jay expressed a concern I often hear from parents.

"No, fortunately, antidepressants are not addictive. The side effects of antidepressant medications are headaches, upset stomach, and, sometimes, thoughts of suicide. Tim told me earlier in the interview that he is not having thoughts of suicide. However, Tim, if you do begin to have thoughts about wanting to kill yourself, will you tell your mother right away?" Tim nodded his head "yes" while continuing to look towards his mother.

"I will be monitoring for these potential side effects each time we meet. Tim should also work with a speech therapist on saying words clearly, and work with his counselor to decrease his nervousness around others. Progress is often slow, so be prepared for small steps of improvement. Pressuring him to speak does not help. He is not being stubborn about speaking, as others may think. While Tim attends our all-day school program, I will coordinate with his teacher regularly about techniques he can use with Tim to aid his speaking aloud. For example, the teacher can offer Tim rewards if he whispers or speaks aloud to the teacher or his classmates.

"At home you can encourage him to greet people outside the family with a nod or a smile, instead of looking away from them.

Remind him that this is expected of him – to greet others with social nonverbal gestures — at this beginning stage of his attempt to change. Have him invite a friend over to play so he can experience interacting with people outside of the family."

• • • • • • • • ● • • • • • • • • • •

Every three months, I saw Tim and his mother to monitor his antidepressant medication and his overall progress. It is two years later and Tim is eleven now. He has turned into a tall, strapping, good-looking boy. His build is in sharp contrast to his timid nature and soft voice.

"Tim, how are you liking school here?" I ask.

Tim turns to his mother and whispers to her, his hand shielding his barely moving lips. The answer was that he likes attending school here. The classroom is small and he and his teacher have connected well.

"Tim, I'm pleased you can answer me through whispers to your mother, and that you can look at me sometimes." While still not able to whisper directly to me, he is more relaxed today.

• • • • • • • • ● • • • • • • • • • •

One day, his teacher brought Tim to his appointment with me because his mother was ill. "Tim, how are you doing in school?" I ask, not expecting a reply, since his mother was not there for him to whisper to.

To my amazement and elation, Tim says in a normal voice, "I got an A on my math paper!"

"Tim, I am proud of you! It is so nice to hear your voice for the first time!" Tim seemed pleased with himself, but also surprised. It was as if the words popped out of him as they do when he is at home. He had forgotten for a moment to let his nervousness hold his words back.

• • • • • • • • ● • • • • • • • • • •

A few weeks later, I was in our clinic hallway outside Tim's classroom.

Tim happened to be in the hallway at the same time. Tim looked at me and said in a normal voice, "My mother is going to make some fudge and I'll bring you some. What day are you here so I can give you some?"

"I'll be here next Monday and I will look forward to having a piece. It is nice to hear your voice again, Tim. Keep up the good work. See you soon," I replied.

I think to myself that the next goal is for him to speak aloud to me when his mother is with him and to speak aloud at school, where he is now able only to speak just above a whisper to his friends and his teacher. I'm always looking for the next small step forward.

· · · · · · · · ● · · · · · · · · · ·

It has been four years since I first met Tim. He can now talk aloud at school, to the clerk at the grocery store, and with his friends on the phone. These are important steps forward for Tim. During one of his appointments with me, he was able to talk aloud to me with his mother present. Another goal was met!

While Tim still becomes angry easily with kids who tease him, his fighting has decreased as he has been able to tell kids, "Back off!" When he was angry at his teacher recently, he told the teacher, "It's none of your business!" By expressing anger in words, he is less likely to express it by fighting.

When Tim's family experienced financial problems because his dad was briefly out of work, Tim stopped talking to me and his teacher and friends. He would nod his head in response to my questions, and tears poured out of his eyes. His temper flared and he picked fights with kids. Thankfully, when the stress at home lessened, he once again began to talk aloud and improved his anger control.

Our clinic's education program has given Tim a safe place to work with his teacher on his education and on his Selective Mutism. In addition to school and appointments with me, his routine included meeting twice a month with his counselor, Marcia. He'd walk into Marcia's office with his head down, go straight to the playing cards, pick them up, and bring them to the table where the two of them would play cards. When Tim answered Marcia's questions, it was at first with nods of his head, then in whispers, and finally aloud. He answered her questions about school, his new friends, and tensions at home. The individual counseling was the most intimate part of the clinic's program, and in these sessions Tim was alone with another human being, talking about his feelings. This intimate setting brought on the most intense anxiety. At times, Tim refused to attend his counseling, saying, "I'll come tomorrow." Yet, these individual sessions were critical to Tim becoming more relaxed around others.

· · · · · · · ● · · · · · · · · · · ·

Tim is fourteen now. Because of his progress in not fighting and in being able to talk aloud at school, he will be transitioning back to public school gradually, starting with mornings at public school and afternoons at our clinic. This will be a test of the progress we have seen at our clinic. Can his improvement be sustained in the public school setting?

As I look ahead to Tim's adulthood, I wonder what he will be like - still shy like his father or able to engage with others like his mother? I feel hopeful about Tim. I wish my classmate, Judy, had had this opportunity some sixty years ago to have her anxiety treated so she could become comfortable around others.

CHAPTER EIGHT

Childhood Posttraumatic Stress Disorder

THIS CHAPTER WILL cover the symptoms children exposed to trauma can have and one boy with whom I worked for several years.

Symptoms of Childhood Posttraumatic Stress Disorder (PTSD)

Following are some examples of extreme events that, if experienced or witnessed by a child or teen, may cause PTSD:

- Vehicle accidents in car, train, plane, boat, bike, etc.
- Natural disasters such as earthquakes, hurricanes, tornadoes
- Man-made tragedies such as bombings or school shootings
- Violent personal attacks such as mugging, rape, torture, kidnapping Witnessing spousal abuse between parents; witnessing stabbing or murder of a friend or family member
- Physical abuse from belt buckle, punch, slap, kick causing bruises, broken bones, skull fractures; burns by cigarettes, hot water
- Sexual molestation, rape
- Emotional and verbal abuse from bullying by peers; degrading remarks by parents or other adults
- Neglect of needs for food, clothing, warmth, cleanliness

Following are the most common symptoms of PTSD:

- Sleep disturbance
- Depression, anxiety

Being easily startled by noises or movements; constantly feeling danger is nearby

- Loss of interest in previous pleasures; detachment; feeling numb
- Trouble feeling affectionate toward others; lack of trust
- Sexualized behaviors due to child molestation
- Irritable; physically aggressive toward others; may imitate the abuser's violence
- Avoiding places or situations that bring back memories of the event
- Daytime flashbacks of visual images and sounds, smells, touch associated with the event as if it is happening again
- Nightmares of the traumatic event as it happened
- Tuning out what is happening around him (dissociating, spacing out)
- Difficulty concentrating on schoolwork
- Worry about dying at a young age
- Regressive behaviors such as thumb-sucking, bedwetting
- Headaches, stomachaches

(adapted from www.childrenshospital.org and www.penn behavioralhealth.org)

Introduction to Child Abuse

Child abuse is a heavy topic, one we prefer not to think about, but one that presses for our attention due to its frequent appearance in the news. Court proceedings against priests in the Catholic Church and leaders of Boy Scouts of America leave us shocked and dismayed. We fear for our children's safety and urgently want to know how to keep them free from harm. The emotional and physical wounds caused by child abuse of all types are deep ones, often with long-lasting effects. Studies of the human brain show that child abuse can damage it, leaving thick scars in its convolutions and changing its chemistry.

How did our country become aware of child abuse? Dr. Henry Kempe, an observant pediatrician in Colorado, first identified and named physical child abuse in the 1970's. He theorized that the bruises and broken bones, skull fractures and deaths that he saw in some children in the emergency room were intentionally inflicted upon them by others, usually their parents. At that time, most people, including doctors, found it hard to believe that a child's parent or caretaker would intentionally harm him. We have, sadly, come to learn differently.

Thus began our acknowledgement of deliberate physical cruelty to children, which led to our awareness of sexual and emotional abuse of children and eventually to the passage of federal laws requiring the reporting of child abuse to the police. Each state set up a Department of Children's Protective Services for these purposes: to investigate reported child abuse, to determine if the reported abuse had likely occurred, to determine who the abuser was, and to ensure that the child was safe from further abuse. The prosecuting attorney's office of each state has the duty to prosecute an abuser.

Required reporting has identified the high incidence of sexual and physical abuse to children. The numbers are alarming and overwhelming. "One million children are confirmed victims of child abuse each year. While traumatic experiences are not common in the lives of most children, approximately three million children each year who have been abused or traumatized in other ways are diagnosed with Posttraumatic Stress Disorder. Posttraumatic Stress Disorder (PTSD) is estimated to affect forty percent of the children in violence-ridden neighborhoods." (www.childrenshospital.org)

Child sexual abuse affects many children: by age 18, 12%-25% of girls and 8-10% of boys have been sexually abused (American Academy of Pediatrics website data). The Centers for Disease Control estimates that 9% of high school students and 20%- 25% of college women have been sexually assaulted (CDC website).

When I interview a child and his family for the first time, one piece of history brings me great relief: the absence of abuse of any kind to the child and the absence of exposure of the child to violence in the home and neighborhood. Why such relief? Because from my experience, the child's psychiatric treatment for his emotional and behavioral problems will be much simpler in the absence of child abuse.

The absence of child abuse means the child is protected from harm by responsible parents and caretakers. A good home means adequate food and shelter; a daytime and bedtime routine; cleanliness and appropriate clothing; play with parents to stimulate brain development; and an absence of being molested, beaten, belittled, or ignored. It means the presence of love and empathy from caretakers, and discipline that is firm but not violent.

Many psychiatric disorders are thought to be inherited. However, there are several exceptions, including PTSD. PTSD does not have a genetic cause, although we often see abuse run in families. Only a damaging environment causes PTSD, either as a result of the trauma of natural disasters (such as hurricanes and tornadoes) or traumas perpetrated by one human against another. While natural disasters cannot be prevented, man-made traumas can be prevented, thus allowing children to grow up in safety, without the black cloud of abuse following them the rest of their lives.

Is it possible to decrease and even to completely eliminate child abuse? What an emotional toll on children would be prevented if we only knew how to prevent child abuse. Children would not suffer and mental health professionals would not need to spend energies on rebuilding the lives of children fractured by physical, emotional, or sexual abuse. Picking up the pieces, helping children heal from abuse once it has been identified and stopped, is a costly and long process. Treatment techniques are in their infancy.

What is our culture doing to prevent child abuse? Early efforts in the medical community involved teaching doctors to identify and report intentional injuries of children to the police and teaching parents that beating their child is a criminal act and will be punished. Teachers and other professionals working with children have been taught to report to the police a child's unexplained bruises or a child's statement about being molested. These are important intervention steps, but can we prevent child abuse?

Here are some government and private programs that have decreased the frequency of child abuse: the early intervention program in Hawaii (www.nurturingparenting.com/research_va and http://fww.org/article/misc/frc.htm); support to families through infant-parent services, affordable and high-quality childcare; time off from work for parents with young children; and classes to improve parenting skills.

To address child sexual abuse, churches, schools and other community organizations are beginning to put in place programs to identify sexual abuse early and stop it from continuing. Following are descriptions of some programs these organizations are using:

- Be A Child's Hero Network (www.beachildshero.com) believes that child sexual abuse can be prevented: "The key to sexual abuse prevention is information, education and guidance… If your child is targeted chances are extremely high that he/she is a person parents trust. Sex offenders generally target children where the risk of getting caught is low…Tell your child that if abuse happens to them to tell adults until the abuse stops."
- The Catholic Church is using a program called VIRTUS (www.virtus.org) to stop sexual abuse of children. It was developed with the assistance of experts in the field of abuse.

Phase I of VIRTUS deals with prevention and early detection and reporting of sexual abuse. It teaches five steps to teachers, parents, volunteers and clergy to prevent sexual abuse:

1. Know the warning signs of child sexual abuse.
2. Control access to children.
3. Monitor child programs.

4. Be aware of how children behave normally and how they behave under stress.
5. Openly communicate within the school or church system concerns the adult has about a child's safety.

The United Methodist Church uses Safe Sanctuaries program (www.safesanctuaries.org).

The Unitarian Universalist Church advocates safe guards on their web page (www.uuworld.org).

Boy Scouts of American has developed a sexual abuse prevention training program under the guidance of Dr. Finkelhor, an expert in child sexual abuse research at the University of New Hampshire (www.scouting.org). However, a recent criminal trial against this organization in Portland, Oregon (January 2011) claims that the training was not mandatory for all volunteer leaders and that abuse of Scouts had occurred.

Other websites that educate parents and other adults about child abuse are:

- American Academy of Pediatrics (www.aap.com/parents)
- www.familywatchdog.us locates sexual offenders on maps.
- www.prevent-abuse-now.com
- National Crime Victims Research and Treatment Center at the Medical University of South Carolina (http://colleges.musc.edu)
- www.childrenshospital.org Children's Hospital Boston
- www.nimh.nih.gov National Institute of Mental Health

Books on Abuse Prevention and Treatment:

- A Very Touching Book" by Jan Hindman (for children)
- "No Is Not Enough" by Caren Adams, et al. (for teens)
- "By Silence Betrayed" by John Crewdson (for adults)
- "Supporting Children with PTSD: A Practical Guide for Teachers and
- Professionals" by David Kinchin and Erica Brown, 2001.

- "Post-traumatic Stress Disorder in Children" by Spencer Eth and Robert S.
- Pynoos (2007)

Healing the Boy With Burns and Bruises

Kasha was physically and emotionally abused while living in an orphanage in Russia. When he was six, he was adopted by Mr. and Mrs. Maloney and brought to America. They called him Ron.

Ron and Mrs. Maloney first sought my help about four years ago when he was twelve. What strikes me about Ron at our first appointment is his shock of hair so blond that most people take a second look. He is handsome, with bright blue eyes and a mischievous smile.

After introducing myself to Ron and his mother, I explain to Ron that I will first ask his mother questions about his background, then later direct questions to him.

"Mrs. Maloney, what is your main concern about Ron today?" I begin. Mrs. Maloney speaks calmly and pleasantly, her demeanor belying what has been a rough road for the family: "His rages. They happen several times a month. He goes into rages over small frustrations like being told 'no'. We have to hold him to keep him from hurting us or breaking things. When we restrain him, he yells, 'You're going to kill me!' We hope some medicine might help calm him down, because he's getting too big to hold.

"Ron locks all the doors in the house for fear someone will break in. He won't swim in our friend's pool because he is convinced there are sharks in the pool. Even at the age of twelve, he's afraid to be at home by himself or in a room alone while we are in the house.

"When Ron is upset, he rocks back and forth. When he was seven, we had to remove the headboard on his bed because his rocking caused it to pound against the wall. We finally understood that rocking was how Ron comforted himself when he lived in the orphanage in Russia."

I turn to Ron to ask him some questions about his early years: "Ron, do you have any memories of when you lived in Russia?"

"All I remember is waving goodbye to my mother. I remember the lake near the orphanage and I remember the blue hospital where I went when I got burned. I know a few Russian words and that Kasha was my name."

Beyond these few memories, Ron has little recall of the first six years of his life. Most children have memories starting from the age of three. But, tragically, abuse often erases childhood memories, the good ones and the bad ones. Studies of child abuse show it affects the size of some areas of the brain, changes levels of certain hormones, and impairs thinking (A. Wilner, "Neuropsychiatry Reviews", June 2008).

"Do you know how your hand got burned?" I ask as I examine the scar on his right hand that extends from the base of his thumb to the base of his pointer finger. I am touching his injury not to repair it, of course, but as an act of the healer showing empathy and emphasizing that this injury is significant in his life.

"No. I don't remember either how I got the bruises on my face that Mom told me I had when she first met me."

"Tell me how you feel now."

"I feel scared all the time. I asked Mom if she feels scared a lot and she said she usually feels safe. That's when I began to wonder if something was wrong with me."

Ron's mother goes on to tell me how in 1998 when she first met her son in Russia, he was cute as a button, shy, and thin, with fresh bruises on his face and a scar on his hand. No one at the orphanage could tell Mrs. Maloney how the bruises and scar on his hand came about.

Combining the slim history the orphanage gave them and a few memories that gradually came back to Ron, Mr. and Mrs. Maloney pieced together that he was brought to the orphanage as an infant by his birth mother. Ron's mother later took him home for a time, then returned him to the orphanage for good when he was four. Ron used to tell them how the bigger kids at the orphanage beat up on him and stole his food. No wonder then that at the Maloney's first meal with Ron in Russia but outside the orphanage, Ron put his chin next to his plate and shoveled the food in as fast as he could.

Mrs. Maloney recalled more of the early years, "At the beginning, Ron had a hard time bonding with me, his father, and our daughter, who is also from Russia. I desperately searched for a professional who could help with the bonding problem. I found a psychologist who worked with us for several years, to the point where Ron successfully bonded with us. Part of the treatment was for us to give him gentle massages to get him comfortable with human touch, and to play interactive games with him. We were told to hold him tightly when he had rages. He would finally calm down after two hours. We were exhausted during those two years, but we are happy with the results. Now he sees a different counselor every week to talk out his feelings and this has helped his rages decrease."

As our first interview draws to a close, I share my understanding of Ron with Ron and his mother: "It appears to me that Ron has Posttraumatic Stress Disorder (PTSD) from the bad experiences he had in Russia—the abandonment by his mother, the lack of food, the beatings by the other kids, and perhaps other abuses we don't know about. The way Ron experiences his trauma symptoms is to feel there are dangers all around him, causing him to be anxious and mistrustful. This feeling of vulnerability leads to Ron's self-protective reaction of rage. He becomes like The Hulk.

"My role is to select a medicine that can help him with his fears and anger problems. There are several medications that sometimes help with PTSD symptoms: antidepressants and anti-anxiety medicines are used to calm the fears, the over alertness to his surroundings, and the flashbacks of PTSD. A flashback is a sudden memory of the abuse that a person experienced. A small dose of an antipsychotic medication may help tone down the rages while Ron is learning through his counseling how to calm himself.

"My role is limited to managing the medications. The counselor plays a different role for Ron and your family. She will help Ron learn to trust that most people will be good to him and not abuse him. She will help him identify his feelings, put them into words, and develop coping skills like relaxation. The counselor will help you understand Ron better and suggest practical ideas for dealing with Ron's behavior. As Ron's surgeon was able to reduce the burn scar between his thumb and pointer finger so that each moves independently of each other, the goal is for the counseling and medications to reduce the emotional scars as much as possible."

Mrs. Maloney agrees to try Ron on an antipsychotic medicine to calm his rages, and we discuss the benefits and side effects of the medicine. We agree to meet again in four weeks to see if the rages have lessened. As they leave my office, I catch a glimpse of Ron's tentative smile.

I admit to feeling a special bond to Ron, because in 1963 as a college student, I traveled to what was then the Soviet Union to study the Russian language. It's funny how travel to a foreign place can leave an indelible mark on a young person – a life-long connection to a strange culture and people. And a connection forty years later to the boy with the shock of blond hair.

· · · · · · · · ● · · · · · · · · · ·

It's six months later, and Ron has been doing better with fewer rages over these six months—that is, until two weeks ago. Now the rages are every day, plus he is scratching his forehead with pieces of wire and banging his head on walls—to create pain, he tells me. Last night a crisis occurred when Ron broke a mirror in his bedroom because he was angry that his mother asked him to take his medicine.

In an effort to understand the sudden and dramatic change of the past two weeks, I ask, "Ron, are you having thoughts about wanting to be dead?"

"Yes, and last night I wanted to cut myself with the pieces of glass from the mirror I broke."

"Ron, to keep you from hurting yourself or your family, I suggest you go to the hospital for a few days."

"I agree," Mrs. Maloney replies. Ron stays quiet.

Ron spends five days on our clinic's psychiatric unit for teens, during which the hospital doctor increases his antipsychotic medicine and adds an antidepressant to help with the depression, anxiety, and

PTSD symptoms. Ron no longer has thoughts of suicide or cutting himself when he returns home.

• • • • • • • • ● • • • • • • • • •

Ron has returned to see me two weeks after his hospitalization. He has had no rages and no thoughts of suicide during this time. I ask Ron what he learned during his stay at the hospital: "I learned to count to ten and go to my room to cool down," he responds.

Mrs. Maloney adds, "It was very scary for our family: the broken mirror, the threats to hurt himself and us. We knew he was safe at the hospital. The new medicine they added at the hospital seems to be helping him."

• • • • • • • • ● • • • • • • • • •

It's two years later and Ron is fifteen, a sophomore in high school. He's been on the same antidepressant and antipsychotic medicines, with some adjustment of the doses when I see him every three months. I have found both Ron and his mother rewarding to work with over these almost three years, watching Ron grow up and gradually improve from the damage of child abuse. Ron has a certain shyness today when his mother gently teases him about a girlfriend – "Oh, Mom, not that!"—and then laughs along with his mother and me. Ron is involved in sports and choir and recently earned his driving permit. His mother is pleased he is becoming a responsible driver. She tells me that when he slides behind the wheel of their van, Ron says with a tone of mockery in his voice, 'Driving is a privilege not a right!'

Ron still becomes angry, but less often and with less intensity, going to his room to calm down instead of threatening to hurt his family. Now he feels safe most of the time and can spend time alone and swim in the neighbor's pool. Rarely does he rock to comfort himself anymore. These are dramatic improvements.

Ron has to work hard to finish his school assignments. Mrs. Maloney had assumed his learning abilities were average because, until this year, his grades were good. Now, in tenth grade, the work is too hard for him, and even with the help of a tutor he is earning D's and F's. So Mrs. Maloney asked the school to determine his intelligence level. His intelligence is low-average, however, not low enough to qualify him for special education services. Learning will likely be a struggle for Ron. Success in music and sports comes more easily, where he has perhaps some natural abilities.

Mrs. Maloney tells me, "The turning point with his rages came when we told Ron we would call the police if he went into a rage where we felt threatened. His counselor suggested this idea and it seems to be helping."

"I try to talk with mom about things that bother me instead of getting upset," Ron says.

"I agree, Ron, that talking about stress will help keep your anger from building up. Be aware, too, that there may be events in your life that will remind you of your abuse in Russia—like seeing a movie about orphans or about kids bullying a child. Then your rage may resurface."

Ron's adoptive parents, as well as those of us who have been given the opportunity to help Ron, can enjoy the fruits of our labor as we watch Ron blossom. What a gift his adoptive parents have given Ron, through their unwavering commitment to and nurturing of him, and their willingness to seek and follow through with mental health services for him. How Ron has enriched their lives as well as mine. America has benefited from the addition of an interesting young citizen to our numbers.

· · · · · · · · ● · · · · · · · · · · ·

It's a year later, and Ron is seventeen, a junior in high school. He still struggles with academics, while his social and sports activities are going well. But one day at school, a classmate pushes Ron as he stands in the hallway putting his books into his locker. Within a split second, Ron becomes The Hulk, going into his old self-defense mode. The sense of danger that began in the orphanage resurfaces, Ron throws a punch, and a fight ensues.

Fortunately, no one is physically hurt, but Ron is humiliated by this fight in front of his classmates and teachers. These eruptions had happened at home, but never in public. Ron was suspended from school for five days. Such an eruption is not unusual in children who have been physically abused: a touch or a push from another person ignites memories of being hit at a younger age, and the child victim strikes back without thinking.

Ron was so embarrassed by his loss of control that he refused to return to school. His parents, his counselor, and I all encouraged and implored him to return to school, but he would not budge.

What can be done? His mother, resourceful as usual, found an on-line high school program that he began to use to earn his high school diploma. I felt sad that Ron would miss his junior and senior proms and walking with his graduating class to receive his diploma. But sometimes, as in Ron's case, there is a sudden change of paths in a child's life. What will that shift lead to? I imagine Ron's proactive mother will provide him with the support he needs to complete his on-line high school program and earn his diploma and perhaps even enter college. Ron has warned his mother and me that when he turns eighteen, he will no longer take the two medicines I have prescribed for him. He wants to try managing his anger without the medicines. At eighteen he will legally be able to make his own medical decisions. I suggest that when he reaches that point, instead of stopping them both suddenly, that we gradually decrease one medicine at a time to see how he feels and behaves. If behaviors worsen, medicines can be restarted if Ron agrees. While Ron wants to be an independent adult, I believe he will listen to feedback from me and his parents about how he is off his psychiatric medications. I predict he will be more open to suggestions than most young adults—primarily because of the trust he has in his parents.

As Ron continues to heal from PTSD, he may reach a point where he needs no psychiatric medications. Ron has shown me that abused children can move towards healing. I wish him and his family well as I leave the clinic to live elsewhere. I look forward to an update from him in a few years by calling the phone number he left with me.

CHAPTER NINE

Childhood Oppositional Defiant Disorder

THIS CHAPTER WILL acquaint you with the symptoms of Oppositional Defiant Disorder (ODD) and the more serious Conduct Disorder. Four boys with whom I worked who have ODD will be discussed.

Oppositional Defiant Disorder Symptoms

- Often loses temper
- Often argues with adults
- Often is defiant or refuses to cooperate with adults' requests/rules Often deliberately annoys others
- Often blames others for his misbehavior or mistakes
- Often easily annoyed by others
- Often angry and resentful
- Often spiteful

Four or more of above must last six months or more.

These behaviors must impair functioning in social, academic settings.

Adapted from American Psychiatric Association DSM-5

Conduct Disorder Symptoms

At least three of the following behaviors over the past twelve months must be present:

- Aggression to people/animals: Bullies, starts physical fights, has used a weapon, physically cruel to people/animals, has stolen while confronting a victim, has forced someone into sexual activity.
- Destruction of property: Set fires with intention of causing serious damage, has deliberately destroyed others' property.
- Deceitfulness or theft: Broken into someone's house, car, building; often lies to obtain goods or favors; has stolen items of large value without confronting a victim.
- Serious violations of rules: Stays out beyond curfew; has run away from home overnight at least twice; is often truant from school.
- These behaviors have impaired functioning in social and academic areas.
- Childhood onset is before age ten. Adolescent onset is after age ten.

Adapted from American Psychiatric Association DSM-5

The Boy Who Kicked Me

As Jack, his mother, and one of our staff, Bob, enter my office on our first meeting, I see Jack is a cute, round-faced, Hispanic-looking boy, a short and stocky almost four-year-old, who does not appear to notice me. I ask him to sit in a chair next to his mother. He ignores me and grabs a Kleenex out of the box on my desk, wads it up and throws it at me. "Please, Jack, don't throw a Kleenex at me," I say in a calm but stern voice.

"How old are you, Jack?" He looks like a cornered alligator trying to find some way to attack me.

"Jack, can you look at me?" He looks briefly at me and holds up four fingers. I am amazed he responds since he seems not to be listening to me.

He picks up a puzzle piece and tries to put it into the wooden puzzle lying on my desk. Frustration grows on his face. "Try this piece here," I suggest, trying to be helpful.

Boom! All the wooden pieces hit the floor as his arm sweeps across my desk. He picks up a small book on my desk and drops it on the floor, apparently set on getting a rise out of me. He pounds on my desk with his fists.

"Would you like to sit on your mother's lap, Jack?" I hope his mother's lap will comfort him in this frightening situation.

He moves next to his mother's leg and she boosts him onto her lap. He seems to be catching his breath for a moment and calms down, but not for long. He slides off her lap and ducks under my large office desk, to a place where I cannot see him. I feel his foot kick my leg. "Ouch!" I yell. "Don't kick me, Jack!"

The kick hurt only a little, but I want Jack to know I don't approve of kicking. Joe's mother, embarrassed that he has kicked the doctor, picks him up and restrains him on her lap, pinning his arms and legs under her arms so that he can't strike her or me. The only weapon left to him is his spit, which he propels into the air towards me, missing me by a few feet.

I feel like I have a swirling tornado in my office! I'm upset that I have been kicked. In my many years of working with kids, miraculously I have never been struck by one—probably because I keep myself an arm's length from an aggressive child such as Jack. But Jack had outsmarted me by hiding under the desk where I could not see his foot draw back in preparation to strike me. Although his mother is embarrassed, she can have the satisfaction of knowing I have experienced an assault such as she receives every day from Jack. She has already shown me the scars on her arms from his bites, scratches, and punches.

Jack's mother begins to sob. "I don't know what to do! I'm exhausted! He cusses at me and screams. He has at least six temper tantrums every evening. He hits and scratches himself. He tortures our dog, and recently he took a knife after me. Last week he threw a chair at one of your staff. He won't fall asleep until three in the morning, and then is up by six. I am at the end of my wits!"

"Jack would be a handful for any parent," I sympathize. I feel great empathy for this mother, tears streaming down her round face. What went wrong with this cute child and his well-intentioned mother?

"Jack's bad temper is just like his Dad's. Jack saw his Dad beat me up and I worried how it would affect him. Finally, about a month ago, I took Jack with me to a women's shelter for safety. Now, Jack and I are in an apartment without his Dad and our lives are better. Jack still visits his Dad every day. He says Jack is normal and has no problems; it's me that has the problems, he says. I can't let his Dad know I am bringing him to you for help."

Bob, the staff person whom I have asked to sit in on the session with us to keep Jack under control, adds, "Jack kicks the kids at the day treatment program and I have to take him into a small room and work with him one on one. After an hour he calms down, but as soon as he rejoins the group, he is hitting the other kids again. Jack never has a moment when he is not violent with the children. When I am alone with him, he will be pleasant for short periods of time, now that he has gotten used to me."

Is Jack's violence coming from imitating his father? Or does he have a heavy set of aggressive genes? Maybe Jack is bipolar, but that is hard to diagnose in a child so young. He probably has Oppositional Defiant Disorder as well as Posttraumatic Stress Disorder resulting from all the violence he has witnessed in his home. I will start some medicines to calm his anger.

• • • • • • • • ● • • • • • • • •

It is now two years since I first saw Jack who is now almost six. As Jack, his mother, and a day treatment staff worker enter my office today, I am pleased to see they are all three smiling. Jack is calm, looks me in the eye, and smiles, his eyes twinkling. His mother looks rested and happy. It's the first time in our many meetings over these two years that I have seen so much contentment from them, although improvement has been gradually coming. I relax and return their smiles. "Now I can enjoy my son," Jack's mother says. "He no longer hits or bites me. He sleeps nine hours and so do I!"

What a journey I have taken with Jack, his mother, and the staff of our day treatment program over these two years! Once Jack's mother no longer let Jack's dad dictate his treatment, she let me try various medications. Small doses of antipsychotic medications that help most kids with anger problems did not help Jack at all. Increasing to higher doses caused Jack to begin to sleep nine hours at night, but he was also sleeping some during the day. I decided there was no alternative but to over-sedate him in order to calm him enough for staff to work with him. After a few weeks of his being calm and over-sedated, I gradually decreased the dose of medicine until he was alert most of the day, but still calm.

Through the day treatment program, Jack gradually learned to express his anger in words instead of actions. He began to listen to staff and follow the classroom routine. He could sit still for story time and be next to another child without striking out at her. His mother improved her discipline by being consistent and restraining him if he did not remain in a four-minute time-out when he was violent to her.

Each time I saw Jack over those two years, I was reminded of the shock and the pain I felt when he kicked my leg. Now, beginning to replace this bad memory, is his smile and shining eyes and the rested look on his mother's face, as well as her obvious enjoyment of her child. This reward is why I do this work.

The Angry, Bright Boy

As I review Rick's chart, I brace myself for a bright but angry five-year-old. An angry child is not unusual among my patients, but a bright child is less common. I have noticed over the years that bright children I have worked with often use their intelligence to manipulate and outsmart their parents in the area of discipline.

Rick is a dark-haired, dark-eyed boy whose handsome appearance is overwhelmed by the hostile behavior that unfolds before my very eyes. As he and his mother enter my office, I make my usual simple request intended to test the child's ability to cooperate and be directed by an adult: "Hi Rick, please sit here, next to your mother." I watch him eye the toys on my bookcase on his way to the chair I am pointing to. An angry scowl is on his face.

He sits, then immediately asks, "Can I play with the toys?"

"No, you can't play with them now, but you can play with them later," I inform him in a pleasant but firm voice. This creates a frustration for any child, and I want to see how he handles frustration.

Rick loses no time in showing me how he deals with frustration. He bangs his head with both hands, then bends forward to bang his head on the wooden arm of the chair, and finally pulls his foot to his head and bangs his shoe against his head. He then yells, "You're mean!"

"Please don't bang your head, Rick! Your brain is inside and it's as soft as Jell-O. You need to protect your brain," I calmly explain. "Your job now, Rick, is to sit in the chair quietly while I ask your mother some questions." Amazingly, he sits quietly, but the scowl remains on his face.

Finally able to turn to Rick's mother, I note that she is a small, young woman with curly brown hair, wearing a blue V-neck shirt and slacks. She has an embarrassed and defeated look on her face. "Tell me your concerns about Rick."

"He is very, very stubborn with me and has been this way since he was two. He tries to bite and kick me any time I say 'no'. I can keep him from hurting me, but now that he is bigger, he pushes his baby sister and I'm afraid he will hurt her. He has at least five temper tantrums a day! The counseling he is in once a week here helped with his anger until a month ago when his father and I separated.

"Another problem is he can't focus on a toy or a book for more than a few seconds and he is always on the go. His preschool teacher saw the hyperactivity at school, too. After a month in preschool, I pulled him out because he began to hit himself in the head and I was embarrassed."

As we review the pregnancy and Rick's infancy, it becomes evident that no concerns arose until he turned two. Rick's mother thinks his dad is ADHD and Bipolar, but neither condition has been confirmed by a psychiatrist.

"Now it's your turn, Rick. Can I ask you a few questions?" Rick in a flash twists around in his chair with his back arched towards me like an angry cat.

"Rick, turn around. The doctor needs to talk to you," his mother firmly directs him. A slow turn follows. As I talk to him, I am surprised that he opens up, showing me his good language skills and his high intelligence. Being the center of my attention pleases him.

Asking kids about suicidal and homicidal ideas is part of my routine in every interview. By the age of four, children have some understanding of death and can respond to the question, "Do you ever think about wanting to be dead or wanting to kill yourself?" I prepare parents for this question since many are shocked to learn that children can think of suicide, and others are concerned that my question will put ideas in their child's head. I explain that when a child has thoughts about suicide, he or she finds relief in sharing them.

Rick's response catches me off guard: "I want to kill myself!"

"And how would you do it?" I ask.

"I'd hit my head on the window or cut off my finger with a lawnmower or take a knife off the kitchen table and stab it in my chest!"

"What are you sad about, Rick? Your Mom looks surprised that you feel like hurting yourself," I reply.

"I had no idea you wanted to hurt yourself, Rick," his mother states with concern.

"I always get in trouble at home," Rick says with a sad look.

"Sometimes dreams help us know what a child is upset about. Rick, can you tell me about a dream you have had when you are asleep?"

Rick eagerly launches into a dream where he is a good cop fighting off bad guys. But the bad guy hurts him. "The ambulance takes me to the hospital to make me well," Rick says, ending his nightmare on a hopeful note of doctors helping to save him.

Children often express their anxiety in dreams of monsters chasing them; usually the child escapes on his own or with the help of a parent. Rick's dream is more sophisticated. Rick knows he is the bad guy, always in trouble at home, but in the dream he makes himself the good guy—however, he is an injured good guy who needs help from the doctor.

"Rick, if you could have any three wishes in the whole world to make you happy, what would they be?"

Rick spews forth his revealing answers: "Police handcuffs for mom so she couldn't spank me. Lots of police cars for my Lego play land, so I could help people."

"And your last wish?" The last wish usually comes from the deepest part of the child.

"I wish my dad would break up with his girlfriend and come back to me and Mom. Daddy broke my heart." Rick begins to cry quietly with great sadness on his face.

"You look very sad, Rick. I see that you miss your Dad a lot. Would you like to play with the toys while I talk to your mom?" Rick's face brightens as he finds some toy cars on my book shelf to play with.

I turn to Rick's mother. "If his thoughts of suicide continue, I may recommend an antidepressant medication when I see him in four weeks.

For now, keep your home free of weapons that he could use to hurt himself and have him see his counselor each week to work on his sadness. I see his tears about missing his Dad washed away the scowl on his face."

· · · · · · ●●●●●●● · · · · · · ·

Over the next few months, Rick's defiant and aggressive behaviors towards his mother improve as she disciplines him consistently and is more sensitive to the sadness he feels. Also, I start him on a stimulant to help his hyperactivity and low focus that his preschool teacher had noticed and these symptoms improve. He is ready for entry into kindergarten with his improved focus and lessened anger and sadness.

The Boy Who Controls His Family

David Jones is a ten-year-old boy I will see today for the first time, along with his mother, Mrs. Jones. As I greet them and invite them into my office, I see David is a tall, thin, handsome boy dressed in slacks and a t-shirt with a logo that says, "I'm the Man." His mother is an attractive blond woman dressed in a cream blouse and black slacks. Unlike many of my patients who are struggling financially, this family appears, from their clothing, to be middleclass, with their basic needs of food, housing, and other necessities likely met.

"Hello, I'm Dr. Manalis. Come in and have a seat. David, I'm going to ask your mother some questions first, and then a little later I will ask you some questions. Mrs. Jones, what concerns do you have about David?"

His mother begins in an anxious voice to explain: "Two days ago David threw towels and pillows at me just because his brother was going to a friend's house to play and David would be left at home with no kids to play with. He gets upset over the smallest things. A few months ago, he got mad at a neighbor boy he was playing with and ran into our house, grabbed a broom and ran out to hit him. If I hadn't stopped David, he would have hit the boy, of this I am certain!" David is listening to his mother and wears a slight smile on his face, unlike most of my child patients, who show distress as parents present a litany of complaints about them to me. While some parents are uncomfortable describing their concerns about a child in front of him, my goal is for the child to know which of their behaviors are unacceptable to their parents. Today, it seems as if David feels he is winning an Academy Award for his impressive behaviors at home!

"And how does David do in school?" I ask.

"He's an A student and is well-behaved at school. His teacher just told me that his classmates love him! His teacher couldn't believe it when I told her how violent he is at home. All I need do is tell him 'no' and he throws an hour-long temper tantrum! Just half an hour ago we were at the mall and he began to nag me for a t-shirt he wanted until I finally gave in and got it for him!"

"So David behaves well at school, but not with you. How does he behave with his father?" I ask.

"Over the last two weeks I have felt so hopeless that I send David to his dad's house when he blows up. He doesn't want to go, but I get him into the car and take him there. He's just as bad at his dad's house, but I don't know what else to do," Mrs. Jones replies.

David turns to me and states matter-of-factly: "When I'm twelve I'm going to live with my Dad." His tone of confidence makes me think he has already discussed this with an attorney or a family court judge.

I reflect to myself that bright kids like David are often difficult to discipline, because they can outsmart and manipulate their parents. I turn back to David's mother. "It sounds like a discipline problem to me. When parents divorce, sometimes their guilt causes them to give in to their children too much." As these words leave my lips, I bite my tongue, wondering if I have made an interpretation of the family dynamics too early. Will David's mother hear my words as a criticism? One of the earliest techniques I learned in my training as a psychiatrist is not to share an insight too early, before a parent feels I am empathic with her dilemma.

"No, I don't believe a lack of discipline is David's problem. I think he is bipolar. He's going to hurt someone if some medicine is not found to calm down his anger!" Mrs. Jones insists.

"Are there any blood relatives of David's who are Bipolar or have anger problems? I ask?

"No," Mrs. Jones replies, "no one in my family or his Dad's family acts this way, but I'm desperate to find some medicine to get his temper under control!"

"The fact that David behaves well at school is not typical for bipolar children. Often they are highly irritable both at home and school, Also Bipolar Disorder often runs in families," I explain.

I'm thinking of parents who frustrate me by refusing to consider medication when I feel it is needed; then there is Mrs. Jones at the other end, demanding medicine for her son when it may not be needed. I decide I can't give David a diagnosis or determine the issue of medication until I learn more about him and his family. Since he has had this anger problem for many years, a few more weeks to sort this out seems reasonable to me.

"Mrs. Jones, Bipolar is a popular diagnosis for kids now a days. The internet is filled with doctors and parents claiming many children are bipolar. The medical literature shows that it is being over-used in children. Bipolar is not an easy diagnosis to make in children; it is a serious diagnosis whose treatment involves strong medications. I would like to get to know David and the family better, before I reach a conclusion on his diagnosis, by meeting with David's father to get his perspectives. Also, I want to check with David's counselor to see what insights he has before I decide on a diagnosis."

"I've waited three months to see you and I expected some action today!" Mrs. Jones replies in an exasperated voice.

"I'm sorry it has not worked out as you had hoped. Feel free to pursue another opinion if you'd like."

Mrs. Jones stands to leave. The atmosphere is strained. David looks pleased that the struggle has shifted from him and his mother to me and his mother. I give Mrs. Jones a prescription for a mild medicine to help David sleep since he's only been sleeping five hours a night. We agree to meet in two weeks.

I hope the family counselor will help David's parents implement effective and consistent discipline. And that David's individual counseling will work on his anger and sadness about his parents' divorce.

· · · · · · ● · · · · · · · ·

It's a month later and I realize David has not returned to see me. I pull his chart to see what the counselor's notes report. I see that David's father has come in for some family sessions with the mother so that they can develop a better system of rules and consequences for David. David in the short run will be unhappy with this shift of power from him to his parents, but in the long run it will bring him a sense of safety from his out-of-control anger. Not giving in to Mrs. Jones' demands for medicines to solve David's anger has allowed her to re-frame David's problem as a discipline problem and not a Bipolar Disorder. However, she may have found another doctor more agreeable to her demands.

CHAPTER TEN

Childhood Autism Spectrum Disorders

THIS CHAPTER WILL explain the differences between mild and moderate to severe Autism. A boy and a teenager with whom I worked will be discussed.

Symptoms of Mild Autism

A. Social Skills are Weak

- There is an interest in others, but social skills are awkward, eye contact is low
- Body language and facial expressions are restricted

B. Communication Skills

- Speech and language skills are near-normal
- There is a lack of ability to understand subtle aspects of language such as humor, sarcasm, and metaphors
- Intelligence is normal or low-normal

C. Unusual Behavior Traits

- Repetitive motions such as hand flapping, twisting
- Preoccupied with switching lights on and off
- Dislikes changes in routine
- Preoccupied with part of an object

- Does not do pretend play such as pretending to talk on a toy phone
- Does not use toys in ways intended, for example, rolling a car on the floor
- Sensitive to loud noises or bright lights
- Dislikes being touched or held

Adapted from DSM-5

Symptoms of Moderate to Severe Autism

A. Social Skills are Weak

- Little or no eye-to-eye contact with others (looks through a person)
- Prefers to play alone, in own world, aloof
- The 2 year-old-does not raise her arms as a gesture to be picked up
- Does not point at object desired
- Does not bring an object to show parent
- Does not smile in response to parent smile
- Does not respond to name being called
- Does not imitate face a parent makes
- Does not play peek-a-boo or hide-and-seek
- Dislikes being touched or held
- Upset by crowds

B. Communication Skills are Minimal or Absent

- No gestures are used to indicate needs
- No words are used to indicate needs
- If language is present, used in odd ways
- If language is present, child does not talk back and forth to another
- If words are used, they are used to repeat another's words
- Takes things literally
- Humor and subtle aspects of language not comprehended

- Odd or unusual phrases
- Mental retardation is common
- Savant ability in one area (for example, memorizes phone books or does advanced math) may be present

C. Unusual Behavior Traits

- Repetitive motions like hand flapping, spinning
- Head banging, toe walking, rocking, biting self
- Makes high-pitched squeals
- Preoccupied with switching lights on and off, spinning objects
- Upset by changes in routine or changes from one activity to another
- Attached to unusual objects (stones, strings)
- Preoccupied with part of a toy such as the wheels of a car
- Does not do pretend play, such as pretending to talk on a toy phone
- Does not use toys in ways intended, for example, rolling a car on the floor
- Sensitive to loud noises or bright lights
- Rages when denied something
- Lines up objects precisely
- Anxious or scared for no obvious reason
- Restricted interests for example, watches same video over and over

Adapted from DSM-5

The Boy With Autism

Let me introduce you to some basic information about Autism before I introduce you to Billy, one of my patients with Autism. Autistic Disorders encompass several degrees of disability, from a mild to a severe set of symptoms. About one out of every fifty nine American children has Autism (Center for Disease Control, 2014).

Autism is a serious disorder of the brain, thought to result from faulty development during fetal growth in the uterus. Boys are affected with Autism four times more often than are girls. The number of children with Autism has been growing dramatically since the 1990's, for unclear reasons. In the year 2000, there were 94,000 autistic American children, while in 2008, there were almost three times that number (www.nimh.nih.gov)! Are children receiving more accurate and earlier diagnosis from the medical community and at school, or is something in the environment causing more children to have Autism? The answer to this question is in great debate.

For years, parent groups were the sole advocates for their autistic children. Between 1943 when Dr. Leo Kanner identified Autism as a distinct diagnosis, and on into the 1970's, psychiatrists blamed Autism on "Refrigerator Mothers." A Refrigerator Mother was defined as one who was aloof and emotionally cold with her infant and thought to interfere with her infant's bonding. However, through recent research, we know that Autism results from faulty connections within the brain, and science has finally stopped blaming mothers for causing Autism.

Over the last several years, pediatricians have been making greater efforts to diagnose autistic children during the toddler years. The hope is that earlier diagnosis will lead to earlier treatment and better outcomes for these children. Mental health professionals may not see autistic children until the children are six or seven years old, while school psychologists will often not see them until they enter the public school system at age five or six. Both teachers and mental health professionals are learning how to be alert to Autism when they first have contact with these children.

But can Autism be diagnosed when a child is one or two years old? This is the challenge currently being taken on by pediatricians as they screen toddlers for Autism. When a toddler is brought to the pediatrician for routine care, the parents are asked to complete a five-minute questionnaire called the Modified Checklist for Autism in Toddlers (MCHAT). If the checklist indicates possible abnormalities and Autism is suspected, the MCHAT should be given again when the child is 24 and then 36 months old. In addition, the child should be referred to the local special education service for an evaluation, as well as to a child psychiatrist or an Autism Clinic for further testing and follow-up.

The MCHAT has many flaws – it may miss an autistic child or it may see a normal child as autistic. More work needs to be done to improve the quality of this checklist so that parents are not told their child may be autistic when in fact she or he is not autistic, or vice-versa, where the autistic child tests as a normal child. (The MCHAT can be found at the website www.dbpeds.org.) Early detection is critical, so that intensive treatment in an Autism program can begin early.

Treatment services for Autism vary across America from not existing in some rural areas, to being weak in others, to excellent comprehensive services available, most often near large cities and universities. Studies show that the more hours per week spent in intensive treatment, the more improvement can occur. A minimum of 25 hours per week is recommended ("Diagnosis of Autism Spectrum Disorders in the First Three Years of Life," Rebecca J. Landa, Ph. D., Nat Clin Pract Neurology 4 (3):2008).

Causes of Autism are thought to involve a combination of genetic and environmental factors. Also playing a role may be birth factors such as older parents, low birth weight, a lack of oxygen for the baby during childbirth and in vitro fertilization. While many parents are still convinced that infant vaccinations cause Autism, recent research shows that this is not the case.

Now I want to introduce you to Billy, an autistic boy I worked with for several years. Billy and his grandmother, Mrs. Roberts, first came to see me when Billy was eight years old. Grandma's gray hair surrounds a pleasant face and she is dressed in a housedress and sturdy shoes. I learn rather quickly that she is a grandmother with a mission, determined to help her grandson reach his full potential.

Billy is a chubby, eight-year-old boy with slicked-back black hair, a clean shirt and slacks, and an avoidance of me as he enters my office with his grandmother. He is smiling, but not at me. He goes directly to my bookcase, which holds a few toys, picking out a doll that he mumbles to while I talk to his grandmother. His presence is like that of a ghost – a murmuring shadow in the room, wandering about the office, doll in hand. "Billy, can you sit in that chair next to your grandmother for me?" I redirect him from his wanderings. Billy understands my request and goes briefly to the chair, but soon is up wandering again. I turn to Billy's Grandmother to gather the details of Billy's life.

"What is your main concern about Billy?" I ask Mrs. Roberts.

Mrs. Roberts starts her story in a frustrated voice. "Well, the school is only letting him attend half days, so he's not learning as much as he could be. His special education teacher complains that he can't sit still and he can't focus very long on his work. I know he is autistic and mentally slow, but he can still learn. I don't like the school slowing down his learning!"

Mrs. Roberts is the kind of persistent advocate every special-needs child deserves. Young children can't advocate for themselves. They depend on parents, grandparents, or other caretakers to find what resources exist in the school and community to help them catch up. Mrs. Roberts wants to maximize the help Billy can receive through the school system.

She and Billy's father take Billy twice a year to the university Autism Clinic where he was diagnosed with Autism at age six. The only local services the family has used are those in his school. Unfortunately, Billy was not referred as an infant by his family doctor to an early-intervention program, where birth to three-year-olds who have delays in speech, motor, learning, or social skills receive free intensive services involving speech, physical therapy, and developmental training. An early program could have helped improve Billy's lax muscle tone, his language skills, and, especially, his social skills, even though he had not yet been diagnosed with Autism.

Billy's school noticed a learning problem during his kindergarten year, which led to him failing kindergarten. When the school tested him at age six, they determined that he was retarded and autistic, so he was placed in special education classes. The university Autism Clinic confirmed these diagnoses.

The school also noticed that his focus was low in kindergarten and now in first grade. His teacher insisted that Billy's father take him to a psychiatrist to see if he had Attention Deficit Hyperactivity

Disorder in addition to his Autism. Mr. Roberts finally agreed to have Billy see me.

Today, Mrs. Roberts is sharing Billy's history with me. "When Billy was a year old, his mother suddenly walked out on him, leaving him for my son to take care of. Since then, I've been his daytime caretaker while his dad works. I remember Billy was upset by loud noises when he and his dad came to live with me. He's always been a fearful child and one not easy to comfort."

"How does he get along with other kids?" I ask.

"Billy would rather play alone, but now he at least tries to play with other kids more than in the past, but he gives up easily. He's obsessed with computer games and plays them constantly instead of spending time with friends – that worries me," Mrs. Roberts says.

I review in my mind the big picture of Billy's late diagnosis and his meager treatment. The late diagnosis of Autism is common in children, and it is because of this that the American Pediatric Association is attempting to have all toddlers screened for Autism using the tool described above.

Once an Autism diagnosis is made, the next question is whether treatment is available near where the child lives.

Billy has been receiving special education services since age six for his academic work, and speech therapy for his delayed language skills, both of which have improved. Twice a year, he visits the distant university Autism Clinic. What has been missing from his treatment is the use of intensive services to increase his interest in others, as well as medications to improve his focus. These years of missed opportunity alarm me. Will I be able to interest Billy's father in play therapy to improve Billy's connections to others and medication to help him concentrate better?

"Billy, what makes you mad sometimes?" I ask.

"When I can't get to level nine on my Star Wars game," Billy replies, eyes averted from me. Grandma has told me earlier how Billy talks in computer game language, like saying "the Ninja kicks the purple dragon." Very little of his talk is about real life.

"Mrs. Roberts, can you give this ADHD checklist to Billy's teacher to complete and return to me? If she reports that he has

SYLVIA A. DYGERT MANALIS, M.D.

eight or more of the eighteen ADHD symptoms, like low focus, hyperactivity, distractibility, and impulsivity, then I will recommend a medication to try if Billy's dad agrees to it. I need to meet Billy's dad next time to get his views of Billy and discuss my ideas with him. I'll review the benefits and side effects of ADHD medicines when you and Billy's dad are here at the next visit. Here's a pamphlet for you and your son to read explaining what ADHD is and how it is treated. Treating Billy's ADHD is the easy part. The harder part is treating Billy's Autism, especially his low eye contact and his lack of interest in making friends. Play therapy for Billy with a counselor may help him become interested in people and learn how to talk back and forth with them. If he has friends he will be less obsessed with playing computer games and watching cartoons."

• • • • • • • • ● • • • • • • • • •

It's a month later, and Billy is taking the ADHD medication I recommended after the teacher checked all eighteen of the eighteen ADHD symptoms on my checklist. Billy's focus is better at school, his grades are improving, and to his grandmother's delight, he is now allowed to attend school all day instead being limited to half-days. Today, Billy arrives with his grandmother as well as his father. Mr. Roberts is a large version of Billy – stocky and short, with basic clothes and a quiet demeanor – but with greater social skills than Billy. We review Mr. Roberts' concerns about Billy and how I view Billy. Mr. Roberts tells me, "Billy seems calmer and is learning better with his new medication."

"It is good that Billy's ADHD symptoms are under control. The new goal is to improve his social skills and decrease the hours he spends playing alone on the computer and watching cartoons. This goal is accomplished through weekly counseling with a social worker or psychologist trained to work with autistic children. The counselor will also work with you and teach you how to play and interact at home with Billy to improve his social interest. I will continue to see Billy for medication management. Are you willing to bring Billy to see a counselor?"

"Well, he sees a counselor at school and that is more convenient than bringing him here," Mr. Roberts replies.

"I understand it is more convenient, but school counselors are not trained in the play therapy techniques used with children with Autism," I clarify.

"Ok," Mr. Roberts replies with little conviction.

When I see Billy and his father every four months, I stress the importance of weekly play therapy. I feel very frustrated and alarmed that precious time is being lost to Mr. Roberts' stubborn refusal to bring his son to counseling. The window of opportunity is closing. What am I missing that could help Billy's dad understand the importance of social skills in a child's life? Perhaps I should set aside my goal and accept their goal of Billy learning more in school and having fewer temper tantrums at home and school.

· · · · · · · · ● · · · · · · · · · ·

When Billy turns nine, he begins overturning desks at school and attacking his teacher. I add an antipsychotic medicine, which calms his anger and has the potential to improve social skills in autistic children. I chose one of the antipsychotic medications that is less likely to cause weight gain. However, as a side effect it can increase his risk for heart disease and diabetes, so blood work will be needed twice a year to monitor his cholesterol and glucose. His anger improves on the antipsychotic medication.

· · · · · · · · ● · · · · · · · · · ·

Billy is ten years old now. He is getting taller, but still has his soft, boyish look. As he, his dad and grandmother enter my office, Billy briefly looks at me and says, "Hi!" This is a hopeful sign as it is different from his usual ignoring me. Later Billy tells me, "I miss my friend, Tommy. He moved away."

Is this evidence of improving social interest, I wonder? I am encouraged. "Billy seems more social with me today. Have you noticed this?"

"Yes, he says 'Hi' to people at school and in stores," his smiling Grandmother tells me.

• • • • • • • • ● • • • • • • • •

Billy is eleven now. He has become more aggressive at home with his father and grandmother – hitting them and threatening to kill them over small things. "Dad is stubborn like a donkey," Billy tells me in a frustrated voice today.

I muse to myself how stubborn his dad has been about the counseling I recommended. If Billy were working with a therapist, he might be able to talk about what makes him angry and about the teasing he experiences at school.

"Mr. Roberts, please bring Billy to work with a counselor on his anger," I advise him once again. "I don't want to use medication alone for his anger when the counseling might help him deal with his frustration and rejection."

• • • • • • • • ● • • • • • • • •

Billy is thirteen now. "Do I have to choke myself to get what I want?" Billy asks me today. This is Billy's new way of expressing his growing frustration. Billy is starting middle school in a building new to him, with new teachers. His adjustment to the new school has been rough: verbal anger expressed toward his teachers; turning over desks; hitting his grandmother and dad at home. This transition to many new changes at school is difficult for Billy. "Last year was more fun," Billy tells me.

Dad is frustrated too. "Last year Billy was in special education classes with higher-functioning kids and he did better and liked it more. I'm going to ask the school to put him into a different class or send him back to his old school."

"I agree that talking to the school about what works better for Billy makes sense," I respond.

• • • • • • • • ● • • • • • • • •

As I review my five years of working with Billy, it is my hope that parents who suspect their child is autistic will seek an early diagnosis from their pediatrician, school, local mental health center as well as a university Autism Clinic and that once the diagnosis is made, parents will immediately find an intensive treatment program with which they can work.

The Teen with Mild Autism

Autistic Disorders encompass several degrees of Autism: mild, moderate and severe. Carl illustrates mild Autism compared to Billy, whose story is found earlier in this chapter, and who has moderate Autism. For general information on Autism, please refer to Billy's story in "The Boy With Autism."

Carl, age fourteen, has benefited from the federal law that requires public schools to provide special education services for autistic children from preschool through high school. Following high school, sheltered workshops provide a place for the autistic adult to work and earn some income. Most autistic adults will be unable to live alone or support themselves, and will live with their family or in group homes for autistic adults (Kantrowitz, Newsweek, November 27, 2006; www.msnbc.msn.com).

I wonder how Carl, the teenager I will write about in this essay, will fare into adulthood. Will he achieve the independence he craves or will he always need a family member's supervision and financial help?

Carl's Autism is mild in that he has fairly good language skills, but still lacking in the important area of subtle aspects of language such as jokes, sarcasm, and metaphors. I see as Carl enters my office today for his first appointment with me that he is a shy boy of fourteen. As I assess his physical appearance, I see he does not look like a typical teenager. His short, neatly combed blond hair, thin, pale face and delicate build are more that of an eleven-year-old than a fourteen-year-old. Where are the bulging biceps and triceps of the teenage young man? Carl's clothes are conservative: a white t-shirt void of logos, khaki pants, and white track shoes; no earring, tattoo, or green-tinted hair. I notice a stiffness in his body and an avoidance of acknowledging my presence.

Carl's mother, who accompanies him today, is a tall, pleasant, blond woman dressed in slacks and a blouse. I will learn that she is a devoted advocate for Carl and has succeeded in finding special services at school and in the community for him. She is recalling for me today, as I ask her about Carl's background, how his diagnosis was first made. "It was his third-grade teacher who first thought that he might be autistic. She was a young teacher and had been taught, unlike Carl's elderly first-grade and second-grade teachers, what to look for – the lack of eye contact, the avoidance of other kids, and his dislike of change – like changing from math to English class. Carl hated lunch and recess, the teacher told me, because the kids called him 'gay.' After the school tested him for Autism, he was placed in special education classes, language therapy, and social skills training. His intelligence is ok. I'm grateful to his young third-grade teacher for taking a special interest in him and getting him the help he needs."

"What was he like as an infant, Mrs. James? Did he gaze into your eyes and smile and did he like to be held and cuddled?"

"Yes, he did all those things as an infant, just like my older son had done. But when he turned two, he suddenly became shy and withdrawn until he had little interest in any of us in the family."

I reflect to myself on the fact that Carl's development was different than that of most autistic children, who show problems bonding during their first few months of life; they fail from the first months to smile and coo at their parents or look into the admiring eyes of their parents.

"It appears to me that you have done a good job of getting Carl the services he needs over the years, Mrs. James, both at school and by having him see a psychologist for several years to work on his social skills. I am wondering why you are bringing him now, at the age of fourteen, to see a psychiatrist."

"Well, he is sad and cries a lot. He's nervous around adults and kids his age and he worries about his homework constantly."

"Carl, can you tell me what you feel sad about?" I ask.

"I feel like I want to be dead sometimes. I got so upset about a school report that I told my teacher I wanted to be dead. I never tried anything to hurt myself. Kids call me names at school and it upsets me. I feel no girl will ever want to marry me because of my Autism. I want to move out on my own when I finish high school and get a job in sports."

"Carl, I'm impressed with how well you can express your sad feelings and I appreciate your honesty with me. To help with your sadness and your worries I would like to have you start some medicine called an antidepressant. It will be important for you, in addition to the medicine, to continue talking to your counselor about your sadness and worries.

"Also, Carl, can I make a suggestion? Remember to look people in the eyes when you talk to them. I know this is uncomfortable for you, but it is very important. It lets the other person know you are really interested in him. Right now, you are looking into my eyes and face, and this is good. Remind yourself over and over: 'eye contact!' I'll plan to meet with you and your mother every few months to see if the medication is helping your sadness and worries about being around other kids."

· · · · · · · · ●· · · · · · · · ·

It is two years later and as Carl enters my office today, I am pleased to see he is wearing the common teen device ear buds attached to his i-Pod player. He seems proud of this sign of adolescence, as he is proud of being on the school track team and volunteering at a park for the summer. Today, Carl is smiling, really almost beaming. This is a far cry from his demeanor at my first meeting with him when he was fourteen and very sad and anxious. However, what has changed very little are his eyes, which still evade mine and only land upon mine briefly while he and I and his mother talk about how his life is progressing at school and at home.

"I finished ninth grade on the honor roll," Carl reports shyly, but with pleasure. "I have some friends now. I suppose next time I see you I'll have a girlfriend." He blushes as he imagines the face of this yet-to-be-found special girl. Carl had his first crush on a girl last year, but never had the courage to sit by her or talk to her, or make the all-important flirtatious eye contact with her.

· · · · · · · ● · · · · · · · · ·

It's a year later and Carl is seventeen years old now and in an eleventh-grade special education program. It has been six month since I last had a session with him and his mother. Today, his body language has a different tone to it than in our past visits. Is it confidence and pride, I wonder to myself, as Carl and his mother take seats across from me? Carl is also looking at me – giving me eye-to-eye contact – not avoiding my gaze as he has in the past. I feel triumphant for Carl.

At the beginning of our fifteen-minute medication review session, I always review what medications he is taking, checking the doses, so we are all on the same page. At our last visit, we agreed that because Carl's depression was much better, he could taper off his antidepressant. I am eager to learn how he has done without it.

Mrs. James explains, "We tried him off the antidepressant for three weeks, but his anxiety when he was with people and his worries about schoolwork both came back, but not his depression. So I restarted his antidepressant four months ago and since then he worries much less."

"Ok," I respond. "It looks like the antidepressant was helping him worry less and be less anxious around people, so let's continue it. And has your depression stayed away, Carl?"

"Yep, I'm not depressed," Carl responds with a slight smile, his eyes meeting mine.

"Tell her about your summer job," his mother urges.

"Well, I earned $2,000! I helped build some buildings at the park."

"That's great, Carl. Did you make any friends?" I ask hopefully.

"Nope! They all thought I was crazy because I talked about the Civil War. But my boss liked history, so we talked."

"What did you do with your $2,000?"

"I saved my money for a while but now it's gone!"

"Oh?"

Mrs. James chimes in as she proudly hands me a photograph she's brought to share with me. "Here he is in his Civil War soldier's outfit he bought with his paychecks. He's standing with a re-enactment brigade!"

"Carl, how handsome you look in your soldier's uniform!" I respond as I examine the photo, also feeling a sense of pride in Carl being able to stay at a job where kids called him crazy, and being able to delay spending his money all summer for this coveted goal he set for himself. And that he has a passion for the Civil War which has connected him to others. Now I know the source of this sense of confidence I hear in his voice and see in his erect posture.

"How are you doing in school?"

"I'm on the honor roll and on the track team again." Carl gives me eye contact without me reminding him. "Wow!" I think to myself.

"Carl, you have much to be proud of. Any girlfriends yet?" It seems I'm always pushing him forward.

"No, but the guys at school are working on that for me," Carl says casually, grinning. I think back to his sadness when he was fourteen and his fear that no girl would ever want him. Now I see an optimism shining through.

Carl's story is the icing on the cake that keeps me working as a child psychiatrist. Progress, small, step-by-small-step, brings Carl to the verge of adulthood, poised perhaps to be at least partly self-sufficient and to perhaps find a young woman who will love him and want to marry him. I hope these both for him.

CHAPTER ELEVEN

Childhood Hallucinations

THIS CHAPTER WILL explain what hallucinations are and will present two children who had hallucinations following the deaths of close relatives.

Symptoms of Hallucinations in Childhood

Hallucinations are experiences thought by the person to be real instead of imaginary and of any of these sensory modes:

- Vision
- Hearing
- Tasting
- Smelling
- Touching

In adults, such imagined experiences often signal serious mental illness. However, in children and adolescents, they are thought by some to be part of normal development and by others to signal the presence of depression, bipolar illness, or schizophrenia.

One study reported that hallucinations occurred in 8-21% of a group of 11-year-olds. Two-thirds of those 11-year-olds with hallucinations had no mental illness; the remaining one-third had depression or other mood disorders, ADHD, disruptive behaviors,

Tourettes Disorder or Obsessive Compulsive Disorder, with only a few suffering from Schizophrenia.

Medical illnesses can also cause hallucinations in children: fever, infection, electrolyte disturbance, brain tumors, migraine headaches, and seizures. Some medicines and other ingested substances can cause hallucinations in children: steroids, stimulants, marijuana, cocaine, and other illegal drugs. Adapted from currentpsychiatry.blogspot.com/2010/10/hallucinations-in-children-diagnostic.html

The Sad Girl Whose Grandfather Beckons to Her

Helen is a pretty, seven-year-old girl with long, curly hair. She is dressed in a plaid, sleeveless sundress that falls below her knees, giving her an elegant Victorian look, except for the finger in her mouth and her occasional baby talk. Her mother, dressed for her job in a fast-food restaurant outfit, has brought Helen to see me for a psychiatric evaluation today.

Helen's mother launches into her biggest worry about Helen. "I am just now finding out that she may have to repeat first grade! The kindergarten teacher last year said Helen was shy and somewhat slow at learning. Now the first grade teacher says she hasn't learned anything this year and school will be out soon!"

"I understand your shock; let's see if we can sort out what may be helpful regarding Helen. The teacher completed my ADHD checklist and reports that Helen has fourteen of the eighteen ADHD symptoms. This suggests that a stimulant medicine might help her focus.

"She may also have a learning disability which can only be identified if you ask the school to test her. Mrs. Frederick, you have the right under a federal law to ask the school to test her for learning problems. I suggest you put in writing, 'I would like my child tested,' and hand it to the principal, keeping a copy for yourself. Your school should do the testing in a timely manner, followed by a meeting to discuss the results with you and tell you if Helen qualifies for special education services from the school. If the school delays, there is a free service that provides you with an advocate to help you talk to the school."

"Helen, how do you like school?" I ask.

"I wish I could learn to read like the other kids!" Helen replies sadly. "Mrs. Frederick, I see the teacher also notes that Helen is sad, keeps to herself, and feels other kids don't like her. Have you noticed her looking sad or crying often?" I ask.

Helen pipes up, "No one likes me at school. Kids call me stupid and ugly. I wish I had some friends. My teacher lets me sit next to her so kids wouldn't pick on me."

"Thank you, Helen, for being open about the teasing you get at school. Mrs. Frederick, I suggest you tell the principal that Helen is being bullied at school and ask what they can do to help. All schools should have an anti-bullying policy in place.** Hopefully, Helen's teacher and principal will explain to the class that bullying is against the school rules. In addition, the teacher and you can encourage Helen to be assertive by learning to speak up, telling a kid, 'Don't call me names! I don't like it!'"

Mrs. Frederick adds, "Helen was timid as a baby and now she is shy around kids. She is shy just like her dad."

"Shyness is one type of temperament we see in infants. The shy infant often has a parent who was shy as a child, so shyness may have a genetic basis. The good news is that shyness can be overcome in most toddlers if parents gently teach the toddler not to be afraid of people. It looks to me like Helen has nicely overcome her shyness with adults. She seems at ease with me today, but may still be shy with her classmates. This can be worked on in counseling through role playing and other techniques."

"What other things make you sad, Helen?"

"Well, I miss my grandpa. He died."

"Yes, my husband's father died two years ago, and he and Helen were very close," Mrs. Frederick adds with tears in her eyes conveying her own deep sense of loss.

"Helen, do you ever hear voices or see people who aren't real?" I ask. "I hear my grandpa's voice saying 'When you die, be with me,'" Helen says.

"Do you think he means join him now or when you get old, Helen?"

"Now," Helen tells me.

"Kids and adults often tell me of hearing voices of a close relative who died recently. We call this an hallucination. For Helen and most kids it is part of the normal grieving process, if it does not last more than a few months. In Helen's case, the voice has lasted two years, so this is of concern and we will keep an eye on it," I explain.

"Do you ever have wishes that you were dead, Helen?"

"Yes, sometime I wish I was dead."

"Do you have a plan of how you would kill yourself?"

"No, I don't," Helen replies.

"Mrs. Frederick, I feel Helen is going through a depression. She has sadness which may have been with her several years and thoughts of suicide. I recommend an antidepressant for Helen. Her difficulty making friends and learning to read, as well as losing her grandfather, have all likely contributed to her depression.

"For now, I suggest we try Helen on a stimulant medication for ADHD and an antidepressant for her depression as well as her shyness. I will see her in a month. Have her see her counselor weekly until then."

· · · · · · ●● ●● · · · · · · · ·

A month has passed and Helen returns with her mother. Her depression is less and she is no longer thinking about suicide or hearing her grandfather's voice. The stimulant medication has improved her focus and her grades are improving. The school is testing her to see if she has learning delays. The school counselor is helping Helen improve her social skills and Helen has a few friends now. Helen's class is being taught that bullying and teasing others is not tolerated by the school. Helen will continue to work weekly with her counselor at our clinic and I will see her every two to three months to monitor her progress and medications.

**Since the shooting of students at Columbine High School in Colorado, most states have required schools to develop anti-bullying policies in which bullying (defined as any behavior directed repeatedly towards a person and intended to cause distress or inflict injury) is against school rules (www.colorado.edu/cspr/safeschools/bullying/overview. html. This movement grew out of research on school shootings that concluded that "seventy one percent of perpetrators of school shootings viewed their acts as retaliation for being bullied by classmates…" (www.Indiana.edu/~safeschl/SrsBullying.pdf).

The Boy Whose Dead Aunt Called to Him

I see my next patient sitting with his mother in the hallway outside my office. I introduce myself and ask, "What is your daughter's name?"

"I'm a boy!" insists the child with two pigtails and a big grin on his face.

"Oh, I'm sorry. Come in the office and we'll get started."

Sam is a handsome, seven-year-old boy with two pigtails of medium length, jeans, and a white cotton shirt. He lives with his mother, grandmother, and two sisters. His dad lives next door and sees Sam every day. Sam has been attending the day treatment program in our clinic for over a year in order to work on his hitting and kicking. This has improved. His teacher and mother decided he should see me for his trouble sitting still in school.

Mrs. Pond launches into her concerns about Sam: "Sam's kindergarten teacher tells me he is not learning, even though he seems smart and this is his second year in kindergarten. She says he is hyperactive. The preschool teachers never complained about Sam at all. The school is testing Sam to see if there is a learning problem."

"I'm glad the school is testing Sam. The testing will tell you his I.Q. and whether he has learning disabilities. Let's have the kindergarten teacher complete my ADHD checklist to see if he has enough symptoms to get the ADHD diagnosis. Do you have any other concerns about Sam?" I ask.

"Ever since Sam's aunt on his dad's side died about eight months ago, Sam has become fearful. He is afraid to go to sleep because of scary dreams about dead people asking him to come to the graveyard," Mrs. Pond responds.

"Sam tell me about your aunt who died."

Sam's face immediately goes from a wide grin to a look of great sadness. "Well, I miss her a lot. I'm afraid to look at the clock she gave me and I'm afraid to touch it. I want to go with my dad to visit her grave, but my friends say ghosts will pull me into the ground!"

"Sam, do you ever hear voices talking to you when no one is around?" I ask.

"I hear my aunt say, 'Come up here and see me.' I see her in my room at night. The dark scares me. I wish she'd come back alive. That's all I wish for," Sam says.

"Hearing voices of a dead relative and seeing the dead relative within a few months of the death is common in children I see, Mrs. Pond. Sam's have continued for eight months – much longer than the average. Also, he has developed some phobias about her death, like avoiding looking at the clock she gave him. If these symptoms show no improvement within the next month, I may recommend an antidepressant medicine to help with his anxiety and phobias. I will ask his counselor to focus on grief work with Sam over this next month. I will be interested in the school test results and the ADHD checklist from the teacher, as well as how Sam's grief work goes, so let's meet again in four weeks to pull all these together and get him in the best shape possible for first grade in the fall. Bye, Sam, see you soon."

· · · · · · ● · · · · · · · ·

When I see Sam and his mother a month later, we review the results of his school testing and the ADHD symptom checklist his teacher filled out for me. I see Sam has a reading disability and an intelligence level of 70, which is low average. The school has recently placed him in special education for these problems. His teacher reported many ADHD symptoms, such as low focus, being highly distractible, impulsivity and, hyperactivity. Mrs. Pond agrees to my suggestion of a stimulant medicine for ADHD.

As Sam and I talk today, he and his mother agree he is less fearful and able to sleep better. He no longer hears his aunt's voice asking him to join her in heaven nor sees her at night. His sadness is lifting. He has been able to visit his aunt's grave with his dad. And his learning should improve as we start the stimulant medicine for ADHD and he continues in special education classes. I do not suggest an antidepressant, I explain to his mother, because his sadness and hallucinations are improving through counseling.

CHAPTER TWELVE

Childhood Gender Dysphoria

THIS CHAPTER WILL present the symptoms of Gender Dysphoria in childhood and will tell the story of one child dealing with this dilemma.

Symptoms of Childhood Gender Dysphoria:

A.   A strong cross-gender identification. In children this is manifested by four or more of the following:
   *   Repeatedly stated desire to be the sex other than one's anatomy
   *   In boys, wears female clothing; in girls, wears masculine clothing Strong preference for cross-sex roles in make-believe play, or fantasies of being the other sex Intense desire to participate in games or hobbies of opposite sex
   *   Strong preference for playmates of the opposite sex

B.   Discomfort with his or her biologic sex
   *   In boys, assertion that his penis or testes are disgusting or will disappear; rejection of rough play or typical boy toys
   *   In girls, rejection of urinating in a sitting position; insisting she will grow a penis or that she does not wish to grow breasts, and dislike of feminine clothing

C. The disturbance does not involve a biologic inter-sex condition
D. The disturbance causes significant distress in social, school, and family settings

Adapted from American Psychiatric Association DSM-5

The Boy Who Wants To Be A Girl

A ten-year-old boy enters my office, his handsome face wearing an engaging smile. Following behind him is his mother, Mrs. Johnson. She says her son, Jake, has Attention Deficit Hyperactivity Disorder and has benefited by being on stimulant medicines in the past, and she wants me to restart his stimulant. As she reviews her list of concerns about Jake—he can't focus and has low grades; he is hyperactive; he steals small things from family members and does not sleep well—she tells me, almost as an after thought, "Jake knows he is a boy, but says he wants to be a girl."

Today Jake looks very much like a boy, dressed in khaki slacks, a neat, white polo shirt and black gym shoes emblazoned with a red Nike logo. His mother first noticed when he was six years old that he preferred to play with girls and with dolls, and liked to play princess and mother roles, wearing long dresses and floppy hats. She had not been very concerned about it and neither had his father.

I explain to Jake and his mother that I have little experience with the wish by a child to be a gender opposite his biological gender. I pull out my psychiatric diagnostic manual (DSM 5, 2013) and turn to Gender Dysphoria, which from 1980 until 2013 was called Gender Identity Disorder. Jake's mother and I review the features needed to meet the diagnosis of Gender Dysphoria. To my amazement, Jake meets every one of them: the genitals of a male, Mrs. Johnson tells me, but the desire to be a girl; a preference to dress in girl's clothing and play female roles in make-believe play; an intense desire to play games traditionally associated with girls; and a strong preference for girl playmates. He also has experienced the required discomfort about being a boy, for more than two years. He does not like sports and he sits like a girl to urinate.

I remember when I was just a couple years out of psychiatric residency training and was still wet behind the ears, an eleven-year-old boy, Bob, who liked to play with dolls and dress up in women's clothes, was brought to me for advice. Back then, in 1976, Gender Identity Disorder had not yet been added to the psychiatric diagnostic manual. I admitted I didn't know much about this problem but thought he might outgrow it, hoping to allay their worries and fears. Now that I know more about Gender Dysphoria, I realize that I should have asked Bob's parents if he had normal male genitals. I should have asked Bob if he hated his penis and testicles and if he wanted to be a girl. I wonder what happened to Bob as he entered adolescence. The odds are that he became homosexual and not transsexual. But let's return to Jake's story.

As I ask Jake more about his wish to be a girl, he clarifies that he only wishes that half the time. The other half he is glad he is a boy. He denies he was ever sexually abused. Jake then tells me about his imaginary friend who is a girl about his age. He tells me of a dream he had about her in which two men kidnapped her, tied her to a chair and threw her off the boat she and Jake were on. He tries to save her, but is not strong enough to overpower the two men. He feels very sad he has lost her in his dream. During the day Jake often feels sad and about once a month he wishes he were dead. He has never tried to kill himself and says, "I would not kill myself."

I agree to put Jake back on his ADHD medicine, which helped his focus and grades in the past. I also suggest he work with a counselor about his boy-girl confusion, which I believe is causing some depression. We set up a follow-up appointment, but they do not return to see me. Perhaps they will seek the ADHD medicine from their family doctor, but for now they are not ready to explore the Gender Dysphoria.

What do we know about Gender Dysphoria in childhood? German psychiatrist A. Korte and colleagues reviewed all the studies on this topic and published the results in Deutsche Arztebl International in 2008. Here is what they found among the few studies that had been done:

1) The incidence of Gender Dysphoria in children and teens is less than one percent. Of children experiencing it, a

minority (between two and twenty percent) are thought to become transsexuals in adulthood.

2) The causes of Gender Dysphoria are in debate according to Korte. Genetic studies do not indicate genetic or hormonal causes dominate. Some researchers believe sexual and physical abuse play a factor; others believe neuroses develop from a poor relationship between mother and child.

3) Korte reports that the treatment of children with Gender Dysphoria is controversial. Most scientists believe the children should be allowed to go through their adolescent sexual development naturally and see where they end up. They oppose the use of hormones or genital surgery prior to adulthood. Rarely do children with Gender Dysphoria go on to retain in adulthood the wish to be of the opposite sex. Many become homosexual in their desires, but remain comfortable with the biology with which they were born.

In 2007, a Berlin clinic developed a team approach to work with children with Gender Dysphoria and their parents. On the team are experts in adolescent psychiatry, sexual medicine, and pediatric endocrinology. Most of the team's patients who wanted to be the sex opposite of their biology were found to be running away from homosexual desires. So the treatment focus was primarily on making the patients comfortable with their homosexuality. For those who are transsexual, genital surgery and hormone treatment was advised to be delayed until adulthood.

The cause of discomfort with one's biologic gender is not understood as of now. An article in The New York Times, August 23, 2015, entitled "How Changeable Is Gender?" by psychiatrist Richard A. Friedman, reports on a study that suggests "transgender people have a brain that is structurally different than the brain of a non-transgender male or female."

A recent book, "Becoming Nicole: The Transformation of an American Family," by Amy Ellis Nutt, tells the fascinating story of her son, who very early in his life wishes to be a girl, and how Ms. Nutt sensitively handles this dilemma.

CHAPTER THIRTEEN

Childhood Disruptive Mood Dysregulation Disorder (DMDD)

The psychiatric term, Disruptive Mood Dysregulation Disorder (DMDD), was a newly created diagnosis in 2013. The term, unfortunately, is a mouthful. I wish that an easier and more descriptive term could have been chosen by those who created it for the Diagnostic and Statistical Manual of Mental Health (DSM-5). Nonetheless, it is a valuable addition.

This new diagnosis was developed for a very important reason: many children with anger problems were mistakenly being diagnosed with Bipolar Disorder because there was no closer diagnosis that fit them. Thankfully, some very important research determined that most of the severely angry children they studied did not become bipolar in their adult years. Rather these angry children grew up to be anxious and depressed adults. Anxiety and depression are much milder problems than bipolar. So even though the anger seen in these children was so destructive and intense, it was not observed to develop into adult bipolar illness.

Anger is a common complaint I hear from parents regarding their children. In fact, it is the most common complaint I hear from parents. Toddlers are known for their temper tantrums and their angry outbursts, however, with good parenting and gradual development of the brain, the anger usually gets modulated and comes under the child's control. There are, however, some children who continue to have intense anger as they enter the preschool years and early grade school years. And these are the children who may fall under this new diagnosis.

Regarding treatment for children with DMDD, the research is in its infancy. Psychotherapy of various types may be helpful as well as medications like antipsychotics, antidepressants, anticonvulsants and stimulants. More research for this problem is critically needed.

Joe's story, told in "When Adoption Does Not Overcome Genetic Disadvantages," will introduce you to the details of this disorder.

Disruptive Mood Dysregulation Disorder Symptoms

- Angry outbursts which are intense and frequent (at least three times per week) and have lasted one year or more
- Starting after age five and before age ten
- Anger is a problem in all settings including home, school and social settings
- Sad, angry, irritable mood almost every day

Adapted from
www.aacap.org, www.nimh.nih.gov and childmind.org

When Adoption Does Not Overcome Genetic Disadvantages

Joe is the kind of kid who I fortunately see only rarely in my practice of psychiatry. A few minutes before I am to meet this eight-year-old boy and his parents for the first time, I scan his mental health chart. My concerns begin to skyrocket. Joe has, in his short life, tried to push his pregnant mother down stairs, and later tried to suffocate the new baby with a pillow. Every daycare he was enrolled in kicked him out because of his attacks on kids and teachers. Joe, fascinated by fire, lights wads of paper in his house. Over my 30 years of psychiatric work, I have seen several young children who burned their homes down while playing with cigarette lighters or matches.

Two of them killed family members, so I know the extensive damage that an unsupervised child with access to fire can cause. I have never seen, on the other hand, a young child bring serious physical harm to family members by their acts of hitting, pushing, or throwing things at them. A child's small size makes serious injuries to adults unlikely. Recently, Joe chased his mother with a kitchen knife, but she was able to wrestle the knife from him. His attempts to injure family members have landed him in a psychiatric hospital three times within this past year.

I go into the hallway to invite Joe, his mother, and his young sisters, ages six years and one year, into my office. Unfortunately, Joe's father has not come to the appointment, probably because he and Joe's mother have recently separated. I prefer to have both parents here to tell me their often-different views of their child and to see how the child connects to each parent —does he, for example, cling to Dad, avoid Mom? Joe surprises me by obediently sitting where I direct him.

Joe is a cute, slight boy, neatly dressed in slacks and a t-shirt. He quietly puts together a puzzle I hand him while I ask his mother, Mrs. Troy, about him. Joe's mother is an attractive woman in her thirties with curly, blond hair, neatly and stylishly dressed. She is amazingly calm and matter-of-fact given all she has been through with Joe and given the recent separation from her husband. I make a mental note that she is good at hiding the distress she must be feeling. Some people are very skilled at this: smiling when they are feeling down or worried. At her feet sits the baby who survived Joe's suffocation attempt, asleep in a car seat. Her older daughter, cute and blond, sits on the floor beside the baby, playing with a doll she brought with her. I wonder how Joe, with his violent nature, has affected his sister's life. After Joe's mother gives more examples of his out-of-control anger, I ask her to tell me about his early years.

Joe was adopted by Mrs. Troy and her husband when Joe was only five days of age. The birth mother had breast fed him for those first five days. I imagine that someone, perhaps the birth mother's parents or Joe's birth father, talked her into placing Joe in an adoptive home against her wishes. It is Mrs. Troy's opinion that this five days of being breastfed by his birth mother made Joe reluctant to bond with Mrs. Troy. I have my doubts about this theory, but I keep them to myself, not wishing to challenge someone I am attempting to build rapport with. Mrs. Troy somehow knows that Joe's birth father is an alcoholic who has been imprisoned three times for assaults on people. I am curious how she knows this detail, since adoption agencies often withhold such significant pieces of family history from adoptive parents. I wonder if Mrs. Troy knew the birth family. I will ask her later about this. My guess is that Joe's anger has a genetic component from his alcoholic, raging birth father.

"An adoption that we had arranged just before we got Joe fell through. I think this caused me to keep my distance from Joe, feeling I could lose him, too," Joe's mother explains. "I feel Joe never bonded with me in those early months of his life. My husband and Joe didn't bond either."

"I want to ask Joe some questions now," I explain as I turn to Joe, who continues to rework the puzzle I have handed him. "Do you ever think about killing yourself, Joe?" I ask.

"Yes, when I have been bad, I wish I was dead," Joe says.

"Do you ever think about killing another person?"

"I think a lot about killing my two little sisters," Joe shares matter-of-factly. "A voice tells me to kill people and do other bad stuff." It appears Joe has hallucinations that could be part of a depression or bipolar disorder or the early stages of schizophrenia. I will gather more information on the hallucinations later.

I ask Joe to tell me about one of his nighttime dreams. "I'm jumping off a building, trying to fly, but I go down, falling and falling, until I wake up." A dream of falling signifies depression, hopelessness, despair. Often kids whose every action brings reprimand and punishment end up feeling evil, like the Devil himself. Psychiatrists used to think kids didn't experience depression, but about two decades ago, that theory was revised—kids do become depressed and some kill themselves out of deep despair.

I turn to Joe's mother to discuss my understanding of Joe and possible treatment approaches. Joe has already been to several psychiatrists who have placed him on practically every psychiatric medicine used in children. Most made his rages worse, his mother thought. I am acquainted with two of the psychiatrists he has seen and know them to be careful and skilled clinicians. At this point, I am considering referring Joe to a medical center where unusually difficult kids are evaluated and treated. I like a challenge, but I try to be aware of the limits of my skills. I will discuss this idea of referral to a medical center with Joe's mother at our next appointment.

I add a new medication to the two he is already on. I want to find a medicine that will help subdue his hallucinations and anger. Antipsychotic medications decrease anger and hallucinations, so I add one. I suggest Joe continue to see the counselor he has worked with this past year, with a goal of helping him feel emotionally closer to his family. Joe's mother has found him a special school program where, if he disrupts his first-grade classroom (which he surely will do), he can be moved into a mental health problems program in the same building, and back and forth as needed. This is an arrangement that will minimize Joe's chance of being kicked out of school completely. I let Mrs. Troy know that her resourcefulness in finding programs for Joe is excellent and gives Joe's situation hope.

I wonder what lies ahead for Joe in the next twenty years. What kind of teenager will he become? What kind of worker, husband, father? His future surely looks bleak. His genetics may be the main problem and no cure yet exists for his aggressive genes.

I regret that I do not know what happened to Joe after I referred him to a medical center. But I can make an educated guess. In his early adult years, he is likely to become an alcoholic and be in prison for assaulting people. He may have spent his youth in psychiatric hospitals and residential treatment programs or in the juvenile justice system. His adoptive mother is likely to be exhausted and have a broken heart; she loved him as if he were her biological child. But while we know that a good home can keep some aggressive genes from being expressed, sometimes the aggressive genes win out over the efforts of good parents. Joe's parents deserve a Medal of Honor for trying to save Joe.

CHAPTER FOURTEEN

Discipline Problems in Young Children

T HIS CHAPTER WILL explain how to discipline young children ages one to five and problem behaviors of preschoolers. Two families who are struggling with their preschoolers come to me for help and end up with very different results.

How to Discipline Toddlers (One- and Two-Year-Olds)

- Begin to use "No" in a firm tone as your one-year-old needs redirection. A firm, forceful tone, rather than yelling or a weak tone, conveys calm disapproval.
- Use eye contact when saying "No." Make your face and eyes look disapproving.
- Redirecting a toddler away from his negative behavior means repeating in words what he needs to do to obtain your approval: "Roll the ball. Do not throw the ball."
- Distracting a toddler often works: "Play with this doll instead of the ball."
- Keep instructions short and simple. "Stop!" instead of "Don't do that or you are in trouble!"
- Try a firm "No!" or redirection or distraction.

If this approach does not work, try the Time Out system:

Hold the two-year-old on a chair in a hallway or in a corner of a room away from the hub of activity. Time outs are thought to work because of the child's isolation away from people and thus loss of attention from people. Once the child is quiet for one or two minutes, the time out ends.

At the end of the time out, put into words the toddler's negative behavior: "You hit me. This is not ok. Do not hit."

- Firmly hold the child in the chair or corner if he will not remain in time out. One- and two-year-olds will need assistance in remaining in time out.
- For a toddler who is hitting and kicking, a lap restraint can be used to prevent injury to others and to calm the child. Place the child on your lap facing away from you. Cross the child's arms over his chest firmly. Cross your legs over the child's legs if he is kicking. Keep a space between your chest and the child's head so he cannot hit you with his head. Hold him until he quiets, then an additional one or two minutes.
- At the end of the restraint, the parent puts into words the toddler's negative behavior: "You hit me. This is not ok. Do not hit."
- Put angry feelings he is having into words for him. Why he is angry should be your best guess based on the situation: "You are mad because I said 'no'." Keep it simple, since toddlers have a limited ability to understand or use words.
- Praise a child often, even regarding small things she does well. "You are sitting quietly at the table, Sally. I like that."
- Give four praise statements for every critical one. THIS IS VERY IMPORTANT!

How to Discipline Preschoolers (Three- to Five-Year-Olds)

- Use "No" in a firm tone when your preschooler breaks a rule. A firm, forceful tone, rather than yelling or a weak tone, conveys calm disapproval.
- Use eye contact when saying "No." Make your face and eyes look disapproving.

- Redirecting the preschooler away from his negative behavior means repeating in words what he needs to do to obtain your approval: "Roll the ball. Do not throw the ball."
- Distracting a preschooler may work: "Play with this doll instead of the ball."
- Keep instructions short and simple. "Stop!" instead of "Don't do that or you are in trouble!"
- Use the Time Out System:

If a firm "No!" or redirection or distraction do not work, give a time out on a chair in a hallway or a corner of a room away from the hub of activity. Time outs are thought to work because of the child's isolation away from people and thus loss of attention from people. Once the child is quiet for three to four minutes, the time out ends.

At the end of the time out, ask the child why he needed the time out. If he does not describe his negative behavior, then the parent puts into words his negative behavior: "You hit me. This is not ok. Do not hit."

Firmly hold the child in the chair or corner if he will not remain in time out. Three-year-olds are usually able to remain in time out without assistance once the parent has trained them to do so.

- Using Lap Restraint System:

For a preschooler who is hitting and kicking, lap restraint can be used to prevent injury to others and to calm the child. Place the child on your lap facing away from you. Cross the child's arms over his chest firmly. Cross your legs over the child's legs if he is kicking. Keep a space between your chest and the child's head so he cannot hit you with his head. Hold him until he quiets, then an additional one or two minutes.

At the end of the restraint, ask the child why he needed the time out. If he does not describe his negative behavior, then the parent puts into words his negative behavior: "You hit me. This is not ok. Do not hit." Put angry feelings he is having into words for him. Why he is angry should be your best guess based on the situation: "You are mad because I said 'no'."

State how he should express his anger next time. "Next time you are mad, tell me 'I'm mad!' instead of hitting me."

- Praise a child often, even regarding small things she does well. "You are sitting quietly at the table, Sally. I like that."
- Give four praise statements for every critical one. THIS IS VERY IMPORTANT

Problem Behaviors of Preschoolers (Three- to Five-Year-Olds)

The following behaviors are a problem when they occur frequently:

- Screaming, kicking, spitting, biting others, throwing items when told "no"
- Throwing self onto the floor and banging feet on floor (frequent temper tantrums)
- Banging head on hard objects; biting self
- Crying or being defiant when told "no"
- Refusing to follow a parent's instruction, for example, "It is time to go to bed,"

Parental Problem Behaviors in Dealing with Young Children (One- to Five-Year-Olds)

- Parent does not state the rule clearly at the child's level of understanding.
- Parent does not give a consequence when a rule is broken.
- Parent gives a consequence some of the time but not consistently.
- Parent yells at or hits a child when angry and frustrated with the child.
- Parent does not verbalize the child's good behaviors.
- Parent makes critical remarks to the child when redirection or distraction would work.

Two Preschoolers With Severe Discipline Problems Whose Parents Respond Very Differently To Discipline Suggestions

As I review the psychiatric chart on Drew, a three and three-quarters-year-old boy, in preparation to interview him, his mother, Mrs. James, and his Aunt Jean, the chart information prepares me for a preschooler with frequent temper tantrums and physical attacks on both family members and daycare staff. Drew and his mother have been working with a counselor on the temper tantrums. Mrs. James feels strongly that medication can stop Drew's serious anger problems, so the counselor has asked me to determine if medication would be helpful to him.

Temper tantrums are normal in the one and two year old child; but when they continue to occur in the three to five year old and include hitting and hurting people, this behavior is no longer normal. Frequent temper tantrums represent an inability of the three to five year old to handle feelings of anger and frustration normally. One common cause of a child's poor handling of his anger and frustration is the parents' lack of discipline skills. Poor discipline can go from one extreme of excessive harshness to the other extreme of giving in to the child's every demand. Knowing how to discipline the one to five year old is not easy by any means. It is a complicated process. Parents who grew up being screamed at and beaten by their parents will be unsure how to discipline; parents who grew up with parents who never said 'no' to them will be equally puzzled about how to discipline. In my experience with families of young children, discipline is the most common problem with which parents struggle.

To see how common a problem discipline is for children of all ages, one has only to watch the excellent television show "Super Nanny". Nanny is not really a nanny at all; she is a British behavior therapist. Each week at the request of a desperate family, Nanny enters a home to help solve the problem of children running the household. The home is one of chaos because the children are talking back to their parents and hitting and kicking family members. The parents are at their wits end. They don't know how to get control of their children and they are feeling miserable about being parents.

Nanny first enters the home and observes the family chaos; next, she puts in place a family routine for each day, like times to awaken, eat meals, do chores, take baths and prepare for bedtime. Nanny knows that children like a routine that is familiar and dependable; it gives them a sense of comfort and security. Next, she explains to the parents and their children the system of discipline called "time out" which is used to deal with children's misbehaviors. How soon peace comes to the household depends on how quickly the parents can learn to discipline their children. Some parents find it very difficult to give up being too lenient or too harsh and Nanny may need to delve deeper into a parent's background to find what is blocking him or her from being able to kindly but firmly say 'no' to a child. Lastly, Nanny sets up some family fun times where parents play with their children and give them positive attention.

Once these steps are in place, the home is magically transformed into an orderly, peaceful one where the children know the rules and consequences and parents feel confident and look forward to fun times with their children. The smiles on the children's faces tell us the children are happy knowing their parents are in charge of the family now.

The Suppernanny show with Jo Frost was a series on ABC which ended in 2011. It was followed by America's Supernanny staring Deborah Tillman on Lifetime television from 2011 to 2013. Both series are currently available on YouTube.

Why is discipline so hard for some parents? Here are some common reasons: parents may think saying 'no' to a child is being cruel or unloving, so they constantly say 'yes' and give in to the child's demands; some parents may think a child can be left on his own to grow as a weed does, without being tended, and that he will learn to control his anger and frustration on his own; others may think, on the other hand, that only spankings and a screaming voice will force the child into submission.

But let's return to Drew and his family's story. Today Drew's mother is concerned about his numerous temper tantrums and his hitting and kicking of family members and day care staff. If a child acts up mainly at home, this tells me the child has some self-control skills. But if he also acts up in the grocery store, at school and other public places as Drew does, this tells me the aggression problem is more entrenched and that his self-control skills are weak.

As I open my office door to invite Drew and his family in, the door is barely open a crack when Drew surprises me by shoving it wider and charging into my office. He is a cute, muscular boy with dark eyes, dark curly hair and a blank expression on his face that is neither happy nor sad nor angry. Drew's slacks and shirt are wrinkled as if he has been rolling on the floor outside my office while waiting for me. His aunt and mother follow him into my office. Aunt Jean is a blond-haired woman with an easy-going look about her. Mother, with brown hair and rumpled clothes, appears harried, as if dealing with Drew in the waiting room has been difficult.

"Hi Drew, I'm Dr. Manalis. Drew, please sit in this chair between your mother and your aunt," I direct calmly and firmly. I am testing Drew's ability to understand a simple request and his ability to cooperate with an adult. Drew moves towards the chair I am pointing at, boosts himself onto it, gathers his short legs under his body and stands on the seat. Suddenly he begins to jump up and down on it. I wait patiently to see how his mother and aunt handle his jumping. I am hoping they will ask him to sit down, but they are silent. "Drew, please **sit** in the chair," I request more firmly. He ignores me and continues to jump up and down between the two women who should be redirecting him.

His mother finally pulls him towards her lap, but Drew shouts, "No!" and continues to jump.

Aunt Jean tries to smooth over her embarrassment about Drew's defiance of my request: "When I tell Drew he is good, he laughs and is happy." Aunt Jean's ignoring of Drew's jumping on the chair suggests to me she believes positive statements about Drew will teach him self-control. Positive statements to a child are, of course, very important, but they do not replace the need to set limits with a child.

"He's smart as a whip," Drew's mother chimes in. Mother, like Aunt Jean, is avoiding dealing with Drew's jumping on my chair. I'm thinking their philosophy on discipline may be the "weed theory," that is, he will develop self-control on his own without parent action.

While Drew and his family waited in the waiting room earlier, my nurse heard the ruckus Drew was making and in desperation grabbed the only toy she could find, a baby rattle and gave it to him. It served to entertain him in the waiting room, but he shakes it throughout my session with him and it is beginning to irritate and distract me. I try to trade the rattle in his hand for a quieter toy, but he clings to the rattle and continues the noise. He is winning all the battles so far.

Mother shares her concerns: "He has lots of temper tantrums. He hits and kicks me, his aunt and his brother and even bites us. At dinner he throws his food."

Drew has decided jumping on the chair is no longer interesting and has crawled off the chair. He finds a puzzle on my book shelf which his aunt is helping him put together. The atmosphere is calmer now.

"Tell me about the pregnancy with Drew," I ask Drew's mother.

I always ask parents about the pregnancy and their child's first year of life. Through the pregnancy history I learn if the child was planned. Long ago I noticed that most kids I work with are not planned, so I decided surprise pregnancies may be the norm and planned ones the exception, so I will research this later. I ask if the parents were at a good spot or a bad spot in their relationship during the pregnancy and whether the mother had medical complications or more than the average pain in the labor and delivery. Was there fetal distress during the hard stages of labor, was the baby blue at birth or was he placed in the intensive care unit from medical complications after the delivery?

As an infant did he eat well, or did he have a weak ability to suck the nipple? Was he colicky? Did he sleep through the night by two months of age or did he cry all night and prevent his parents from getting a good night's rest during that first year? These factors all contribute to the difficulty or ease with which a child begins life and these factors can influence the attitude the parents have towards their infant. For example, a mother whose labor was more painful and prolonged than the average, might harbor angry feelings toward her newborn which can interfere with her bonding with the baby.

"Well, it was an upsetting time for me," Drew's mother shares. "Drew's father beat me and he never helped me with the baby. Since Drew was fussy and didn't sleep much, I never slept. My sister was my only help. Drew's father left us to fend for ourselves when Drew was a year old."

Such a chaotic beginning for Drew, I think to myself. Is Drew's mother's love for him blocked or tainted with bitterness from this difficult time in her life? Or is her guilt about his chaotic beginning blocking her ability to be firm with him? These are speculations I hold in my mind until the picture of Drew and his mother is flushed out with more details. At this point I am favoring the latter theory, that she is permissive and lets him do as he pleases because of her guilt.

On a philosophical note I do not believe the sins of Drew's father (his abuse to Drew's mother) shall be visited upon the son. I believe every child, whether born out of a long-term, loving relationship or out of a brief, casual one, or even out of a violent act of rape, is an innocent being and arrives with a clean slate upon which he and his family environment write his destiny. This, I admit, flies in the face of the powerful influence of genes passed on to a child by both parents. But studies show that a positive family environment can keep violent genes from being activated or expressed in a child. Drew will need a loving, firm upbringing to keep the violent genes silent. He will need to learn from his mother and other adults to control his anger so that he does not become an abusive person like his father.

Drew's mother and I begin to discuss the treatment options for Drew. "My recommendation is for you and Drew to continue working with your counselor on using time outs for Drew's misbehaviors and restraints when he hits and kicks others. The counselor will explain these techniques to you and practice them with you and Drew. I am not recommending medication for Drew."

"But don't you have a medicine to make him stop hitting and kicking us? He's so violent!"

"Unfortunately, we do not have medicine that will teach Drew control of his anger. But a consistent discipline program will help him gain self-control and teach him to express his anger in words instead of action. I'd like to meet with you and Drew again in four weeks to see what progress you are both making in counseling and discipline skills."

Drew's mother, even though disappointed there is no magic pill for Drew's defiance and aggression, agrees to return in four weeks.

· · · · · · ●●● ● ●●● · · · · · · ·

It is four weeks later and Drew and his family are back to see me. I'm hoping for good news. I open the door for them and Drew bolts into my office kicking! He swings his short, stubby legs with intention, kicking at his older brother, Peter, his Aunt Jean and his mother. He swings his hands to slap them. Drew is like a robot that continues his slapping and kicking without needing to catch his breath.

"Mrs. James, you need to restrain Drew! I do not allow kicking or hitting in my office!" It appears that Mrs. James has not learned about discipline from her recent counseling with Drew and his counselor. Mrs. James laughs and makes a half-hearted attempt to pull Drew onto her lap. "Why are you laughing? Drew is kicking his brother and you and his aunt! This is not acceptable!" I announce in alarm, wanting Mrs. James to know how serious this situation is.

"I'm not laughing at that," she says quietly.

"Your nervous laughter encourages Drew to continue his kicking and hitting. He thinks you like his violence. You need to restrain him on your lap. Can I show you how to restrain him by demonstrating with your older son?" She does not answer, so after asking Peter's permission and reassuring him I will not hurt him, I pull him onto my lap and gently cross Peter's arms across his chest and hold him firmly in a lap restraint.

Mrs. James, with Drew on her lap, half-heartedly copies my motions. "He just needs a strong medicine!" she insists. She holds Drew so loosely that he slides off her lap and onto the floor. He rolls towards me and I realize **I** am his next target.

SYLVIA A. DYGERT MANALIS, M.D.

My rule for my own safety is to keep just beyond an arm's length from a hitting and kicking child like Drew. But I am stuck in a corner and can back up no further. As Drew raises his hand to slap me I firmly grab his wrist in mid-air, turn him and place him on my lap to do the lap restraint his mother was asked to do.

"Don't grab him like that!" she screams at me, implying I have hurt him. "I am not hurting Drew by restraining him. Restraining Drew is my way to tell him that his hurtful behavior can be stopped by an adult. I will not allow him to hit me."

My lap restraint has calmed Drew. I release him from the restraint and he slides off my lap and goes to his mother. Suddenly I realize that Drew's mother sees discipline as hurting a child instead of helping him. My attempt to teach her discipline techniques is falling on deaf ears. The step needed before she can take a look at her ineffective discipline will be working with a counselor about the hardships in her own life. This will likely be a long road. Can she trust a counselor to help her? Only time will tell.

"I'm sorry that I have no medicine to help Drew with his anger problem. I hope you and Drew will continue to work with Drew's counselor. I know disciplining a child is a hard task, but with your strong commitment to Drew, things can get better."

Mrs. James gathers her family and leaves, clearly unhappy with me. I say goodbye and close the door behind them. Finally it is quiet and the chaos is gone. I take a deep breath and try to think things through. I feel bad that I cannot connect with Drew's mother. But I felt giving in to Mrs. James' demand for medication for Drew was not the solution to Drew's problems. I had to set a limit with Mrs. James, which is exactly what I am asking her to do with Drew: set limits!

There is no medicine that will do the hard work of discipline, of setting limits and giving consequences. I know that Drew, whose good language skills I observed, can learn to express his anger verbally: "I'm mad!" instead of hitting and kicking his mother. But curbing his physical expression of anger by using time outs and restraints, will be the impetus for the development of his verbal expression of anger.

• • • • • • • ● • • • • • • •

It's a few weeks later and I'm seeing another three year old boy, Frank, who has a problem identical to Drew's: he often throws temper tantrums when told no and throws objects, bites and pinches his mother and father and spits on them when he can't get his way. Frank has an involved father, while Drew does not. Two parents can help each other in this difficult task of discipline, while a single parent has this task all alone. Frank's mother and father became aware by working with Drew's counselor that their discipline skills were weak, so they took parenting classes where they learned how to give children rules and consequences. Drew's mother, on the other hand, is not aware she needs to improve her parenting skills. Frank's parents have been using time outs for several months and Frank is still getting used to the new system.

"Can I play with the toys?" Frank asks right after he, his mother and his father enter my office.

"You cannot play with them now, but you can play with them later," I respond. I use this denial to test a child's ability to resist playing with my toys which sit temptingly across the room on a shelf. "Frank, please sit in the chair between your mother and father."

Frank cooperates with me as he sits in the chair between his mother and father. But within seconds he erupts, spitting at his mother and calling me the "B" word. Like a flash of lightening his rage at being told 'No' by me lights up the room.

"Why don't you restrain him on your lap facing away from you so he can't spit on you?" I explain the lap restraint to Frank's parents. They listen carefully, then mother holds Frank in a restraint on her lap until he calms and stops spitting. "Now sit in the chair, Frank," his mother firmly directs him. A few reminders are needed to keep him in the chair, but he obeys. Success!

Later when I give him permission to play, he chooses a book and says, "Read a book." His language skills seem good, perhaps advanced, so expressing his anger verbally can be expected to replace his physical explosions with proper guidance from his parents and counselor.

Frank's mother and father and I agree that Frank does not need medication. They see the problem the same as I do – consistent discipline is needed. The driving force for change is mother's pregnancy. Soon they will have two children and they want Frank to be able to follow their rules before the new baby arrives. They don't have much time, but they are on the right path to helping Frank gain self-control.

It is a pleasure to see improvement in the discipline skills of parents. Some parents, like Drew's mother, sadly, are not ready for change. Just as there is no magic pill for discipline, there is also no magic pill for readiness to change. A gentle counselor can try to nudge Drew's mother to discover what blocks her ability to set limits with Drew. Can Mrs. James trust a counselor to help her? Or will she drop out of counseling, with painful consequences for her child?

CHAPTER FIFTEEN

Thoughts on Grandparents as Parents, Children's Dreams and Suicide

IN THIS CHAPTER I have included several topics I have found interesting over my years of working with families. I hope they will be informative for the reader.

Grandparents Raising Their Grandchildren

Grandchildren have a powerful emotional pull on their grandparents. I know this from my own experience as a grandmother. My grandchildren's innocence and spontaneity are magical, returning me to a spirit of playfulness I haven't felt since my childhood. Their physical and intellectual growth amaze me. While being a grandmother is more than wonderful, I would not wish to be a parent to them unless, of course, it became necessary, then would I?… I would.

When did grandparents begin to be full-time caretakers of their grandchildren? I remember being told that my grandparents raised their granddaughter after the untimely death of both of her parents. Over the centuries, when children were in need of parent figures, grandparents or other family members stepped up.

In 1970, three percent of American children lived in a grandparent's home. Over the next thirty years, this figure doubled, so that in 2000, six percent of children lived with a grandparent. In just the past ten years, this number has grown even more rapidly, to nine percent of grandchildren living with a grandparent, as reported by the Pew Research Center in 2010.

The many grandparents I have worked with while serving as a psychiatrist to their grandchildren have been forced by circumstances to be full-time caretakers of their grandchildren. What creates these circumstances? Why do children leave the care of their parents? Some situations are temporary: a teen mother may live with her parents, who then assist in the care of the infant until the teen finishes high school and is ready to take on parenting full-time. If a single parent or two married parents join the military and are deployed, they may leave their children behind in the care of grandparents until they return to resume care of them in a few months or years. A divorce or job loss may bring a young family to the grandparents' home for a time.

Other situations are not temporary. Drug abuse by a parent may cause placement of a child with grandparents, for instance. If an infant is born with cocaine in its system, this indicates that the mother is abusing cocaine. This causes some states to remove the child from the mother at birth and place him with a relative or foster family. The infant may return to his mother if she completes a drug treatment program; or parental rights may be terminated and a permanent home found for the child. One grandmother recently told me she went to court to gain custody of her six-month-old grandchild, who had been placed from the hospital into foster care because of the presence of cocaine in his system at birth. The state determined that reunification with the mother was not possible, so placement was made with the grandmother once she came forward.

In other situations, someone reports a suspicion of child abuse or neglect to the police or to Children's Protective Services. If it is determined that a child is being abused or neglected, he may be removed from the parents and placed in a foster home or with a relative. The child will be returned to the parents if the home situation is determined to be safe; if not, the state will search for a permanent home, grandparents being one option in the search.

Less frequently, one parent has killed another parent, so that the surviving parent spends his or her life in prison. I worked with one family in which this tragedy had happened, the father killing the mother. The murdered woman's brother and mother divided up the four children, two each, and raised them, providing support to each other along the way. Or, both parents may be incarcerated at the same time, leaving the children in need of caretakers. When parents are afflicted with severe mental illness or addictions, grandparents may step in to care for the children, at first temporarily, although this sometimes evolves into a permanent situation.

Grandparents from both sides of the child's family may work together, sharing the burden that raising young children brings. But sometimes grandparents struggle in court over who is awarded guardianship of the grandchildren.

If you are nearing retirement and looking forward to having time for your hobbies and time to rest, and suddenly your three grandchildren are left on your doorstep, what will you do? Or if you are 55 years old, still holding down a full-time job, and are presented with this dilemma, what will you do? If you are 65 and your grandchild is five, you will be 80 when she is 20. How is your health? Will you be there until your grandchild reaches independence? These are difficult questions that require careful consideration.

· · · · · · · · ● · · · · · · · · · ·

When I first meet Mark and his grandmother, he is six years old. The state has made Mrs. Perry, his paternal grandmother, Mark's legal guardian. He is a cute, dark-haired, wiry boy with a mischievous look in his eyes. His grandmother is an attractive woman in her fifties, still working full-time. She is committed to providing a stable home for Mark to see him through his childhood and teen years. She appears to be in good health (not using a cane, a walker, or a wheelchair as do some of the grandparents I have worked with), and she will, hopefully, live the 20 years before Mark is out on his own.

Fortunately, Mrs. Perry formed a bond with Mark during the first two years of his life, when he lived with his parents. In these early visits with her son and daughter-in-law, she observed with great concern the heavy alcohol use by Mark's mother during the pregnancy, and by both parents during Mark's infancy, and she was concerned that he wasn't being well cared for. She never noticed bruises on him, but she did notice that his walking and talking skills seemed delayed. When he was two years old, the state removed Mark from his parents, alleging neglect of his physical needs. Someone had reported a concern to the authorities and the court placed Mark with Mrs. Perry.

Mark has lived with his grandmother for four years, over half of his six years of life. Mrs. Perry told me at our first appointment that Mark was erupting with four or five temper tantrums a day, kicking and pinching his grandmother, and being verbally defiant to her. The school teacher complained that he could not sit still in class or focus on his work. His learning was falling behind. Mark was visiting his mother, but only under the supervision of an agency. After these visits, Mark's aggressive behaviors worsened. Mark's father rarely made contact with Mark or Mrs. Perry.

"Mrs. Perry," I summarized at the end of our first visit, "I want Mark to continue to see his counselor each week to help him learn to express his anger and worries in words instead of hitting others and having temper tantrums. The counselor will first help him identify what makes him mad and worried, then she will help him put these feelings into words so he can say, 'I'm mad Johnny called me four eyes at school today,' instead of acting out his anger by hitting someone. The counselor will teach you how to practice with him at home by role playing. The counselor will also help you with your discipline of Mark, making sure it is consistent and effective.

"In addition, let's consider some medications that might be helpful. First, medicine for his hyperactivity and short focus, which the teacher reported, will help his Attention Deficit Hyperactivity Disorder. Second, since Mark is receiving adequate discipline from you, our next step for his anger is medicine, allowing time for his internal controls to strengthen."

"Ok," Mrs. Perry agrees. "I'm desperate and will try anything! I'm getting worn out!"

We discuss the benefits and the possible side effects of these two medicines.

"Also, Mrs. Perry, please ask the school to test Mark to see if he has any learning disabilities for which they can give him special help. There is a federal law which allows you to request this testing be done by the school and requires the school to act on your request. Since we know his mother used alcohol during the pregnancy, this raises his chances of having both learning disabilities and ADHD."

Over the next year, as we work together, Mark's ability to put his anger and sadness into words improves as he cooperates with counseling. His temper tantrums and defiance lessen to the point that I am able to stop his anger medication. He continues to need the ADHD medicine in order to focus in class. The school testing showed that his intelligence was average and he had no learning disabilities, but special education was recommended based on his diagnosis of ADHD. He was placed in a small classroom of four children, with a special education teacher, and soon made the honor roll. Mark continued to work with his counselor at our clinic, especially as he very much missed his father, who rarely visited him, and he missed his mother and her parents, who had dropped out of his life completely.

Life was better for Mark and his grandmother for a year or so, until Mark's grandmother developed medical symptoms and began seeing a doctor to sort out her health problems. Mark sensed this stress and began again to have temper tantrums at home, but he continued to do well at school in spite of his worries about his grandmother.

"Who will take care of Mark if you become unable to take care of him?" I asked Mrs. Perry on a recent visit.

"My daughter and I have planned for Mark to go live with her and her family if I become ill."

"Yep, I like Aunt Joanne. I spend the night there sometimes," Mark replied. "But I'm worried about Grandma. Will she be all right?"

Time will tell, I think to myself. Time will tell. It always does. I'm glad they have a back-up plan and that Mark knows there will be a familiar adult to finish raising him if his grandmother becomes seriously ill.

•••••••••●•••••••••

Rita is a cute girl with multiple braids tied in colorful ribbons, who wears a red dress and a smile. She is being raised by her paternal grandmother, Mrs. Simmon, a tall, stylish woman, and her grandfather. As you will see, Rita's family situation is less stable than Mark's. At birth, Rita was under the care of her mother. Then the mother, because she was struggling with drug addictions, gave Rita to the father to raise. Rita's father did not want to have Rita fulltime, so he asked his mother to take Rita, making her the legal guardian.

But this situation did not work smoothly, because when Rita's father picked her up for what were to be short visits, he often failed to bring her back to her grandmother for several weeks or even months. During that time, he did not allow Rita to see or talk to her grandmother. So now, when Rita's father calls her and says he will be coming to pick her up for a visit, Mrs. Simmon is fearful he will never bring Rita back. Rita doesn't sleep well during these times. The lives of Rita and her grandparents are precarious, controlled by the father's whims. They are trapped in a vicious cycle of uncertainty and anxiety. My major concern for Rita was how to introduce and maintain stability in her life.

Once she starts kindergarten, if this pattern continues and her school attendance is erratic, the truant officer will hopefully become involved in assessing her living situation. A court would then determine which home is best for Rita to give her stability and ensure good school attendance.

Until a truant officer becomes involved with Rita, the temporary guardianship which Mrs. Simmon now has is one which the father can withdraw at any time. The only way the grandmother can get permanent custody as opposed to temporary guardianship is to retain a lawyer and go before a judge. But Mrs. Simmon fears the judge might take Rita away from her and send Rita to live with her father permanently. Courts generally give parents priority over grandparents unless the parents are abusive or neglectful. This is a risk Mrs. Simmon is not prepared to take right now. The court would evaluate what living situation is in the best interests of the child in terms of stability and nurturing. Rita's father might convince the court that his home is best for his daughter. I encourage Mrs. Simmon to consult a lawyer to help her sort out her options and hopefully bring stability to Rita and to herself. Most grandparents I work with have been given custody of their grandchildren through the courts and this cannot change without a return to court. The most stable situation is that in which grandparents adopt a grandchild after the court has terminated the parental rights of the child's mother and father.

· · · · · · ● · · · · · · · · ·

Timmy is a handsome boy with short-cropped blond hair, who, I soon learn, is unusually open in sharing his thoughts, his feelings, and his fantasies with me. This makes my work easier. Timmy was two months shy of turning five when I first met him and his maternal grandmother, Mrs. Todd. He had lived with her since he was one year of age. Timmy had been developing nicely, doing well at home and in preschool, until a horrific event occurred. His step-grandfather, who was helping to raise him these last four years, was stabbed by Timmy's birth mother and her boyfriend when they tried to rob him at the gas station he owned. Mr. Todd was still in the hospital when I first met Timmy. Timmy had not witnessed the stabbing, but he and Mrs. Todd had entered the gas station as the police arrived, and they saw the grandfather on the ground, bleeding, the policemen gathered around him. Timmy's mother was caught by the police and later sentenced to thirty years in jail. So not only had his grandfather been seriously injured and he would be absent as he recovered from his injuries, but, in addition, Timmy's occasional contact with his mother would end. After this overwhelming event, Timmy often took several hours to fall asleep, then would awaken throughout the night. He now insisted on sleeping with his grandmother, whereas before he slept alone. At school, he spit on a child, and at home he threatened to hit his grandmother. In addition to Timmy behaving in ways unlike his old self, he was having nightmares, one of a policeman shooting his grandfather and blood being everywhere.

Before living with his grandparents, Timmy spent his first year of life with his mother, who often left him with various friends and even with strangers. How his needs were neglected and whether he was abused is unknown. Mrs. Todd kept him on weekends during that first year and never saw bruises on him. Around his first birthday, he became very ill with a blood infection and was hospitalized. From the hospital, he was discharged directly to the full-time care of Mrs. Todd. I am not sure if the state ordered this, or if his mother agreed she could not take care of him and handed his care over to her mother. After that, his mother visited him rarely and only under the supervision of his grandmother.

Timmy was seeing a counselor at our clinic to help him talk about his fears and nightmares. I recommended some medicine to help him sleep. I also recommended he talk to his grandfather by phone until they were able to be reunited.

When I saw Timmy and his grandmother a month later, he was sleeping better and was being more cooperative with Mrs. Todd. His grandfather had gone to live with a relative far away to finish healing, but was mailing Timmy cards. Timmy would often cry and say he missed his grandfather and his mother and her boyfriend. Sometimes he would pick up a butter knife and hold it to his neck, re-creating the stabbing his grandfather had experienced. Timmy told me about seeing a monster with bloody hands trying to eat him: "I put a knife on his neck and twisted his head off! I knocked him down!" This was not a dream, but a daytime vision. He recently had told his grandmother that he wanted to die because his grandfather was living far away from him.

Timmy continued seeing his counselor each week, but I did not see him until six months later. Mrs. Todd had been called to court about the stabbing often, so she was busy, and in addition to this, Timmy was being more cooperative at school and home. Yet, he was still crying often, missing his mother and grandfather, although he was sleeping ten hours a night now. His dreams continued to show anxiety: monsters with knives were chasing him. He would tell Mrs. Todd: "Mommy shouldn't hurt Grandpa."

When Timmy turned six and entered kindergarten, the teacher reported he had trouble focusing and sitting still. His grandmother agreed to try some medicine for ADHD, which proved to be helpful. His grades began to improve. By the winter of his kindergarten year, Timmy was no longer having nightmares; he was sleeping well without medication. He visited with his grandfather and spoke on the phone with him often, but he had no contact with his mother, who was in prison for the stabbing. His biologic father and paternal grandparents began to take an interest in him and to visit him. This gave Timmy additional love and support and proved to be critical as his guardian's health began to fail.

The Goldmine of Children's Dreams

Children's nighttime dreams are full of important information about their inner psychological worlds. If you are a parent who wants to understand your child's inner psychological state, then mine the gold that comes from his or her nighttime dreams. Dreams will guide you and your child in deciding which daytime problems are of greatest importance to the child.

Fear is the most common feeling expressed in children's dreams. Fear is seen in a dream of being chased by a monster or bugs; being caught in a storm or kidnapped; someone breaking into the child's home and killing his whole family to name a few. Next in frequency are dreams of anger, then sadness (e.g., falling off mountains or cliffs) and, least often, of happiness. Posttraumatic Stress Disorder dreams are copies of the traumas that happened to the child or teen. These are often dreams that re-occur for the child.

Pamela Blosser states in her book "What Children's Dreams Tell Us" (www.som.org/4family/childdreams.htm): "Parents who learn to interpret dreams open an expanded world for themselves and their children. They can help them solve problems. They can know when their child is troubled and what that trouble is related to."

Dr. Alan Siegel's (www.dreamwisdom.info) book "Dreamcatching: Every Parent's Guide To Exploring And Understanding Children's Dreams And Nightmares," which he wrote in 1998, states: "Most children's nightmares are a normal part of coping with changes in our lives ….. like entering school, moving, living through a divorce or remarriage of parents."

Dr Siegel states that frequency of nightmares is higher in children than in adults. Nightmares are common in children ages two to six. By ages seven and eight, about one out of ten children have a nightmare each week. Fewer dreams are reported by children ages 11 to 14, especially by boys. The frequency of nightmares increases during periods of family stress or family crisis, Dr. Siegel believes.

Many children recall their dreams and will share them spontaneously with a parent upon awakening. Others will need parents to ask, "What did you dream about last night?" Just assume there was a dream. Do not ask, "Did you have a dream last night?" Asking that way often results in the response, "I don't remember."

Once your child shares a dream, ask her what the strongest feeling was that she had in the dream as she was dreaming. Was it a happy feeling, a sad one, a scared one, or a mad feeling? If the child cannot pick a feeling, the parent can suggest a feeling that the dream conveys. For example, "You were having fun at the beach with all of us in your dream, so was that happy?" A happy dream can set a parent's mind at ease that her child is in a good place emotionally.

If your child is not able to think of a daytime stress that may connect to her dream, the parent, knowing what family or school stresses are happening, can suggest a possible source of the child's worries. Listen to your child's response to your suggestion to see if it fits. If that is not the right one, suggest another event in your lives that may ring true for your child.

Let's take an example of Sarah, a four-year-old, as she stretches in bed, trying to wake up: "Mom, I'm scared! I had a bad dream that a big red monster was chasing me!"

"That sounds scary, Sarah. Did he catch you, or did you get away?" you ask.

"I ran away from him, but he was fast and ate me up!"

"That sounds very scary! Did Dad or I try to help you?" Mom asks.

"No! I was all by myself," Sarah says.

"Maybe your dream is saying you are worried about something," Mom explains.

"I don't know if I have a worry, Mom," Sarah says.

"Well, maybe you are worried about starting kindergarten next week. You will be at a new school, with a new teacher and new kids. That can feel scary," Mom suggests.

"I hope my friend Madelyn will be in my class," Sarah says.

"Yes, she will be in your class, your teacher told me, and tomorrow we are going to visit your new school and meet your new teacher," Mom says.

"Will you stay with me tomorrow? Do they have a playground at my new school?" Sarah asks.

"Yes, I will stay with you on the tour tomorrow and I am sure they have a nice playground for when you have recess. Why don't we get in the car today and drive by your new school so we can see it and the playground," Mom suggests.

"Ok, Mom. I feel better now," Sarah sighs with relief.

So Sarah's nightmare expressed her hidden fears about starting kindergarten and allowed her mother and Sarah to talk together about difficult events coming up for Sarah.

Dreams! What gold mines they are!

My Experiences With Suicide

Grief-stricken by the suicide attempt of his musician friend, Robert Schumann, Johannes Brahms wrote his haunting Piano Quartet in C Minor. Listening to the quartet's dark and stormy sounds at the beautiful Chicago Symphony Hall, sad thoughts came to me of my beloved teacher from medical school—a brilliant and caring teacher and physician—who had killed himself recently, many years after our work together when I was a medical school student. I was in shock and grief at the loss of this physician whom I looked up to as a young medical student. I wondered now, as a psychiatrist of forty years, could his death have been prevented? "Tragic" and "senseless" are the words that swarm into my mind when I learn of a suicide.

Over the forty years of my career, my child and adult patients have shared their thoughts with me of ending their lives during periods of deep depression. Some people believe an individual should have the right to end his or her life, whether in the midst of a depression or from the unending pain of a terminal illness. I disagree with this if the person is depressed. Depression is a treatable illness and is transient in most of my patients. While depression may seem interminable to the despondent person, the only thing that makes it forever is a successful suicide.

The sadness of the Piano Quartet brought memories of my many experiences with suicidal patients. As a young doctor, I began a four-year residency at the University of Cincinnati to specialize in psychiatry. One term, I was assigned to work with a psychiatrist, Dr. Smith, as he made rounds on his hospitalized adult patients. One of his patients, a man in his forties, was admitted to the psychiatric unit of the hospital in a manic state. He was a handsome, intelligent man, but agitated, talking a mile a minute on many unrelated topics. Dr Smith started his patient on lithium, which magically calmed the mania, and within a few days, this patient was discharged to his home. A few weeks later, I was shocked to learn from my mentor that his patient was dead from a self-inflicted bullet to his head. As his mania had subsided, a deadly depression set in. I was very upset by this death. In the blink of an eye, his life was extinguished: my first personal experience with the tragedy of suicide.

During another term in my psychiatric training, I was assigned to work in the emergency room of a large general hospital, evaluating people in emotional crises. A strikingly beautiful, black woman in her thirties came in late one night after taking a small overdose of aspirin. As I interviewed her, she denied that she wanted to be dead and I noted that the amount of aspirin she had taken did not require medical treatment. I had to decide that night whether she should be sent home and referred to our outpatient psychotherapy clinic, or if she needed to be admitted to the psychiatric ward in order to keep her safe. I sent her home, convinced by her that she was not suicidal and that her overdose had been done to draw attention to herself.

The next day, I was told that several hours after I had seen her, an ambulance brought her back to the hospital DOA (dead on arrival). I was upset and blamed myself for sending her home. I sought out my supervisor, who explained to me that people who have decided beyond any doubt to end life will tell the doctor they want to live.

The troubling experience with the emergency room patient taught me a great deal. I learned to ask more questions, such as questions about past thoughts of suicide and past suicide plans and attempts. I learned to ask more about the current suicide attempt: did the patient attempt it in front of another person, or notify someone right after the attempt, or was it done in complete secrecy? I learned that while women more often than men take harmless overdoses of pills, I must take seriously their desperation and not discount it as "drama" or a wish for attention. Someone taking an overdose— even a harmless amount—is in distress and needs close supervision until life again feels enjoyable.

I remember a red-haired teenage boy lying on a gurney in the hospital hallway following an overdose of pills. My mentor asked him, "Are you glad you are alive?" Without any hesitation, and to my alarm and surprise, he answered, "No." He had taken his overdose of pills in secret in his bedroom and was found unconscious by his mother when she came in to say goodnight. I learned over my years of psychiatric work that most of my patients who attempted suicide are glad they are alive following the suicide attempt. Only the deeply despondent are not happy they survived. Guiding a suicidal patient safely through the dangerous waters of wanting to be dead was a task to which I became fully committed.

After my training was completed, I started a private practice in psychiatry. I took care of a teenage boy whose father was well-known in Cincinnati. I was somewhat intimidated by his father's high status, but I made my best effort to help Ted with his depression and thoughts of suicide. He became depressed during his parents' divorce. Back then in the 1970's, the antidepressant medications available were, unfortunately, deadly if taken in overdose. I started Ted on antidepressant medicine during his hospital stay and sent him home once he was free of suicidal thoughts, warning his father to closely supervise his use of the pills, as they could be lethal if many were taken all at once. Ted was to follow up with me in a week. A few days later on a Saturday night, Ted's sister became concerned about him because he did not answer his phone. She desperately went looking for him and finally found him unconscious from an overdose of his antidepressant medication. He was rushed to the emergency room and his life was saved, thanks to his sister's concern for him. I learned to emphasize even more the lethal risk the antidepressants of that era brought. I also learned to give patients only one week's dose of antidepressants at a time if I had concern. Fortunately, the Eli Lily Company developed Prozac, which did not have this lethal potential. Many lives were saved as a result.

Once I called a friend about his depression. His family doctor had placed him on an antidepressant and he was in counseling. After talking to my friend, I realized that I forgot to ask him if he were having thoughts of suicide and if he had a suicide plan. I would certainly have asked a patient these questions, but had avoided that with a friend. I called him back. He shared that he had thoughts of wishing he were dead, but had no plan, so inside I breathed a sigh of relief. Most people fear asking a friend or family member who is depressed if they are thinking about suicide. "Always ask." is my motto. I encourage parents to ask their children and teens who are sad, "Do you wish you were dead? Do you have a plan? What is your plan? Have you found the tools (guns, rope, pills, knives, car, etc.) to kill yourself?" Getting these thoughts into the open can help: the depressed person feels heard and the listener can seek professional help for the suicidal person. Suicide can be prevented if a caring person knows what to ask and do.

The cliff over which one can fall into a deep depression is nearby for some when loneliness and despair overwhelm. When a person decides to end his life by killing himself, we are shocked. Yet, who among us has not felt the pull toward the peacefulness of death at some time in our lives?

My dad thought of suicide when he was eighty-five. The deterioration of his body—unsteady walking, dizzy spells, a weak bladder, and seizures—as well as my mother's increasing dementia were depressing him. One day I decided to have a difficult talk with Dad. My sister, who was taking care of my parents, had alerted me to a recent matter-of-fact statement Dad made to her: "Mom and I will sit in the car in the garage with the motor running and the garage door shut and go peacefully together."

I was shocked that he had said this, and I felt nervous about opening up this topic with my own dad. As we talked about his carbon monoxide plan, I empathized with his sadness about his body deteriorating and his loathing of needing to depend upon others. "We enjoy having you in our lives, your active mind, your sense of humor, your wisdom and love. We want you to live as long as you can." I asked if we could secure the car keys and the rifle he kept in the house, to assure us he would not kill himself and he agreed to this.

Dad moved beyond his black feelings about growing old and committed himself to making the most of what time he had left. I was grateful he stayed with us until he died quietly at home, in his own bed, with his wife and my sister at his side at the age of ninety-six. He set a good example for his children, grandchildren, and great grandchildren, for aging with dignity and allowing his life to end naturally.

Appendix

Symptom List With Associated Psychiatric Diagnoses

ANXIOUS, WORRIED, CLINGING, FEARFUL
Adjustment Disorder
Acute Stress Disorder
Post Traumatic Stress Disorder
Generalized Anxiety Disorder
Social Phobia
Depressive Disorder
Selective Mutism
Panic Disorder
Obsessive Compulsive Disorder
Phobias

APPETITE CHANGES
Eating Disorder (Anorexia Nervosa, Bulimia Nervosa)
Depressive Disorder can increase or decrease appetite
Anxiety Disorder

BEHAVIOR PROBLEMS (aggression, impulsive)
Adjustment Disorder with disturbance of conduct
Oppositional Defiant Disorder
Conduct Disorder

Impulse Disorder
Intermittent Explosive Disorder
Trichotillomania
Disruptive Mood Dysregulation Disorder

CONCENTRATION PROBLEMS
Attention Deficit Disorder
Attention Deficit Hyperactivity Disorder
Depressive Disorder
Anxiety Disorder

DISSOCIATION (tuning out)
Dissociation Disorder
Depersonalization Disorder
Dissociation Identity Disorder (Formerly
called Multiple Personality Disorder)
Dissociation Fugue Disorder
Dissociation Amnesia Disorder

HALLUCINATIONS (HEARING/SEEING THINGS NOT REAL)
Depressive Disorder
Manic Depression Disorder (Bipolar Disorder)
Schizophrenia
Severe stress can cause a brief psychosis Abuse of
certain drugs can cause hallucinations

HYPERACTIVE BEHAVIORS
Attention Deficit Hyperactivity Disorder
Anxiety Disorder

IRRITABLE
Depressive Disorder
Manic Depressive Disorder (Bipolar Disorder)
Drug Abuse
Disruptive Mood Dysregulation Disorder

LEARNING PROBLEMS
Low intellect
Learning Disability
Communication/Language Disorders
Stuttering
Gross and Fine Motor Delays

MOOD SWINGS (from sad to euphoric)
Manic Depressive Disorder (Bipolar Disorder)
Adjustment Disorder with depressed or anxious mood
Depressive Disorder

NIGHTMARES
Anxiety Disorder (dream of being chased, being killed)
Post Traumatic Stress Disorder (the dream repeats
what happened in the traumatic experience)
Depressive Disorder (dream of loss or death)
Parasomnias: Nightmare Disorder, Sleep Terror
Disorder, Sleepwalking Disorder

SOCIAL PROBLEMS
Social Anxiety Disorder
Generalized Anxiety Disorder
Panic Disorder
Autistic Spectrum Disorders
Depressive Disorder (isolation, withdrawal)

SLEEP PROBLEMS
Depressive Disorder can increase or decrease sleep
Anxiety Disorder (may delay onset of asleep)
Manic Depressive Disorder (24 to 48 hours
without sleeping and still feels energized)
Narcolepsy

SUICIDAL THOUGHTS
Depressive Disorder
Manic Depressive Disorder
Schizophrenia

TICS
Tourettes Syndrome
Chronic Motor or Vocal Tic Disorder
Transient Tic Disorder
Other Tic Disorders